NEW BIOLOGY
IV

New Biology

IV

edited by
M. L. JOHNSON
and
MICHAEL ABERCROMBIE

PENGUIN BOOKS

1948

First published March, 1948

Photogravure plates printed by
Eric Bemrose Ltd., Liverpool

Made and printed in Great Britain
for Penguin Books Ltd., West Drayton, Middlesex
by C. Nicholls & Company Limited
London Manchester Reading

Contents

Hybrid Vigour *by* Eric Ashby   9

Are Statistics Really Vital? *by* R. B. Fisher   26

Insect Menace to Stored Products
    by John A. Freeman   48

The Biology and Properties of Wood
    by E. W. J. Phillips   74

Vital Statistics of Fish Populations
    by G. L. Kesteven   99

Milk: its Formation and Secretion
    by F. H. Malpress   119

Human Teeth and their Decay
    by Shirley Hughes   143

Glossary   158

Our Contributors   160

Hybrid Vigour

BY ERIC ASHBY

Photogravure illustrations between pp. 64 and 65.

Introduction.

HYBRID VIGOUR is one of Nature's conjuring tricks. Generally when two dissimilar varieties of plants are crossed, the offspring are intermediate in size between the parents. But some pairs of plants when crossed produce offspring vastly bigger than either parent, with a more luxuriant growth of leaves and stems, and with more fruit. Among animals, too, this unexpected bonus in size appears after some crosses. It is as though Nature were giving something for nothing. This phenomenon is called hybrid vigour.

A simple example of hybrid vigour is illustrated in Plate 1. In the middle of the picture is a typical plant of the hybrid between two inbred parent strains of maize. On either side are typical plants of each of the parents. All three plants were grown for the same period in the same soil during the same season. Thousands of examples similar to this can be found in the literature of plant and animal breeding.

The first large-scale systematic study of hybrid vigour was made by Darwin and published in 1876. Darwin compared the average heights of inbred parents and their hybrid offspring for fifty-seven species of plants. Many of his crosses, which included *Salvia, Eschscholtzia*, morning glory, pinks, lupins, peas, tobacco, and maize, showed hybrid vigour. Since Darwin's time an immense amount of quantitative work has been done on the size of hybrids; a random sample of numerical examples is set out in the accompanying table.

Hybrid vigour manifests itself not only as greater weight

9

TABLE I

Some examples of the advantage in size conferred by hybrid vigour.

Organism	Measure	Mean size of parents.		Mean size of hybrid offspring.
Maize	weight (grams)	7.6	17.4	66.0
Maize	height (inches)	85.0	70.0	117.0
Tobacco	height (inches)	30	52	67
Tomato	weight (grams)	47.1	157.1	274.3
Guinea Pigs	weight (grams)	800	420	890
Pigs	weight (pounds)	185.5		228.0

and height; some hybrids show larger seed, more efficient germination, greater resistance to disease, earlier flowering, higher yields of fruit, and greater length of life, than their parents. It is not surprising, therefore, that hybrid vigour makes a strong appeal to agriculturists. For centuries American Indians have increased their yields of corn by growing seeds which are the offspring of dissimilar parents, and in the last fifteen years the amount of hybrid maize sown in the Corn Belt of the United States has increased from 0.2 per cent (1933) to 82.5 per cent (1944) of the total acreage. In Russia and in America first generation hybrids of tobacco and tomato are grown commercially in order to take advantage of their vigour. Even among animals, where breeding is apt to be more difficult, hybrid vigour has been exploited. Crosses between the zebu and familiar types of cattle are being developed for the hard climate of north Australia; and crosses between Jersey Black Giant poultry and White Leghorns are useful, not because the hybrids are larger than their parents, but because they lay more eggs.

Although hybrid vigour is so familiar to biologists, and its manifestations are so spectacular, its causes are not completely understood. Vigour was first attributed to a 'stimulus,' arising from the very process of cross-fertilisation between the male element of one variety and the female element of another variety. This, of course, is not an explanation: it is only a description of the phenomenon in other words. Darwin showed that even the description was incorrect. By a series of simple experiments he proved that hybrid vigour does not occur after crossing unless the parents are dissimilar in their hereditary make-up. This was a very important discovery, for it indicated that the cause of hybrid vigour lay in the hereditary difference between parents, and not in the mere act of crossing the parents. In this incomplete state our knowledge of hybrid vigour remained for thirty years, until the rediscovery of Mendel's work brought about an intellectual revolution, and gave birth to the science of genetics.

A Digression on Genetics

Under the elaborate (one is tempted to call it rococo) superstructure of modern genetics, it is still possible to distinguish the beautiful simplicity of Mendel's original discoveries. They remain at the foundation of genetics and in their simple form they are still adequate to explain a great many instances of inheritance. For the discussion of hybrid vigour, it is necessary to be familiar with the modern interpretation of Mendelian laws. The following paragraphs contain a miniature, as it were, of modern Mendelism, which will provide the reader with the equipment he needs for the rest of this essay.

(i) The unfertilised egg of a female organism carries a specific number of microscopic, string-like bodies, called chromosomes. Not only is the number of chromosomes characteristic of the species, but every chromosome has a characteristic shape and size.

(ii) The male sex cell of the same kind of organism, which unites with the egg on fertilisation, carries the same specific number of chromosomes almost exactly similar to those in the female.

(iii) Therefore the fertilised egg, which results from the fusion of male and female sex cells, contains a double set of chromosomes, each chromosome having a partner. This is called the diploid condition.

(iv) As the organism grows every cell in it receives a replica of the double set of chromosomes.

(v) When sex cells are formed again, the double set of chromosomes is, as it were, shuffled, and divided again into single sets, one per sex cell. Sex cells are said to be in the haploid condition.

(vi) Along the length of each chromosome, in a fixed order and at fixed distances apart, lie the so-called genes, which determine the detailed programme of development of the organism. The geneticist labels each gene by some major effect it has on the organism (*e.g.* it may determine flower colour or eye colour or leaf shape). However, in addition to its major effect, every gene has a multitude of minor effects, and these depend very much upon the influence of the other genes present.

(vii) Since most organisms carry a paired set of similar chromosomes, there will be two genes present for each major effect. The genes may be similar or dissimilar. Pairs of genes are called alleles. If they are dissimilar the effects of one (called the recessive gene or allele) are usually completely suppressed by the effects of the other (called the dominant gene or allele). Geneticists commonly write the dominant allele of a pair as a capital letter (*e.g.* T for tallness), and the recessive allele as a small letter (*e.g.* t for dwarfness). A diploid plant with two similar alleles (*e.g.* TT or tt) is said to be homozygous for T or t. A diploid plant with two dissimilar alleles (*e.g.* Tt) is said to be heterozygous for T and t. If T is dominant to t, then a plant with the gene-composition Tt is indistinguishable in height from a plant with the gene-composition TT; one 'dose' of T is enough to establish tallness.

(viii) The sex cells carry to the offspring whole chromosomes, which are chains of genes. Therefore genes are linked in inheritance, and their several major effects will often appear to be coupled together in inheritance. In fact these gene linkages are frequently broken because chromosomes frequently break and reunite to pieces of their partner chromosome; this complicates, but it does not destroy, coupling in inheritance.

The Genetical Interpretation of Hybrid Vigour

With this very slender equipment of genetics, let us return to the problem of hybrid vigour.

Darwin's work indicated that hereditary differences between parents, and not merely the stimulus of fertilisation, determined whether hybrid vigour would or would not appear in the offspring, but he was not able to suggest what sort of hereditary differences were involved. On the basis of Mendelism it is easy to make a formal explanation of hybrid vigour, assuming very simple and plausible hereditary differences. For instance, the height of a plant depends upon the number of nodes (*i.e.* points on the stem from which leaves arise) and the average distance between the nodes. Suppose node number is controlled by a pair of genes on one chromosome, *N*, *n*, which produce 10 nodes in the dominant condition (*NN* or *Nn*) and 8 nodes in the recessive condition (*nn*); and suppose distance between nodes is controlled by another pair of genes on another chromosome, *L*, *l*, which produce internodes 10 cm. long in the dominant condition (*LL* or *Ll*) and internodes 8 cm. long in the recessive condition (*ll*). Suppose further that there are two parent plants, one carrying the genes *NN ll*, and the other carrying the genes *nn LL*. Both these parents would be 80 cm. tall (though for different reasons). Suppose finally that they are hybridised as follows :

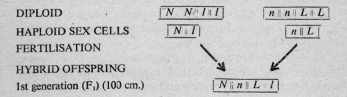

PARENT A (80 cm.)   PARENT B (80 cm.)

DIPLOID

HAPLOID SEX CELLS

FERTILISATION

HYBRID OFFSPRING
1st generation (F₁) (100 cm.)

On account of the assumed dominance of *N* over *n* and *L* over *l*, the offspring (known as the F₁ generation) would

have 10 nodes on an average 10 cm. apart, and would therefore be 100 cm. tall, considerably taller than either parent.
Here is something more substantial than a 'stimulus'; it is
a simple genetical basis for hybrid vigour. According to this
interpretation, each parent contributes to the hybrid different dominant genes favourable to development. What we
have described for height would, on this interpretation, take
place for other characteristics of the plant, through other
genes. The hybrid is vigorous because it is more highly
endowed with favourable dominant genes than either of its
parents.

If there were nothing more to hybrid vigour than this, the
consequences to plant and animal breeding would be immense; for it should be possible to obtain by breeding and
selection a plant with the gene composition $NN\ LL$. In such
a plant as this hybrid vigour (insofar as it affects height)
would be 'fixed.' Provided such a plant were inbred, it
would indefinitely give progeny of the composition $NN\ LL$,
and ther.fore the progeny would indefinitely be abnormally
tall.

In the last four decades hundreds of plant breeders have
joined in the pursuit of permanent hybrid vigour; but it
has eluded them. This elusiveness is one of the peculiarities
of hybrid vigour; no matter how skilfully a hybrid crop is
grown and selected in the first generation, its vigour is
considerably less in the second generation, and inevitably diminishes in each succeeding generation. It seems
impossible to recover and to preserve a homozygous dominant for vigour. On the simple explanation suggested above
it ought to be possible: we therefore have to conclude that
the explanation is inadequate.

In 1917 a distinguished American geneticist, D. F. Jones,
modified the simple genetical explanation to meet this
objection. His modification is still accepted (with some reservations) as the most plausible genetical explanation of
hybrid vigour. Jones' proposals may be summarized under
four heads: (i) Though size may be determined to some

extent by a few 'master' genes, it is in fact influenced by a very large number (perhaps thousands) of other genes. (ii) No inbred parent has a monopoly of genes favourable to development; its chromosomes carry an assortment of favourable and unfavourable genes, linked together. Two dissimilar parents are certain to carry on their chromosomes a dissimilar assortment of favourable and unfavourable genes. (iii) As a rule genes favourable to development are dominant over their alleles unfavourable to development. (iv) On these three assumptions there will be a unique combination of the favourable genes (and a unique masking of the unfavourable genes) from both parents in the first generation after crossing. Every individual in this generation has the same genetic constitution and would show the same degree of hybrid vigour. In the second generation the optimum combination of favourable genes will occur only in a few of the individuals. Most of the individuals in the second generation will have fewer favourable dominants and more unmasked unfavourable recessives than appeared in the first generation; therefore the average amount of vigour will be much less than in the first generation.

These four proposals need to be illustrated by a simplified example, which is merely an extension of the example set out on page 13. Suppose height is determined by twelve allelic pairs of genes (Aa, Bb, Cc, Dd, .. Mm) distributed on four chromosomes, and suppose the chromosomes do not break and unite with their partners between one generation and the next. Then two hypothetical parents may be represented as:

PARENT 1

AA dd HH kk
bb EE ii LL
CC ff JJ mm

PARENT 2

aa DD hh KK
BB ee II ll
cc FF jj MM

and their sex cells will be:

PARENT 1   PARENT 2

A	d	H	k		a	D	h	K
b	E	i	L		B	e	I	l
C	f	J	m		c	F	j	M

If the dominant genes (in the homozygous or heterozygous state) provide 2 units toward height and the recessive genes (in the absence of dominants) provide 1 unit, and if the contributions from different genes are additive (both these assumptions are greatly simplified) then the height of both parents can be written as 18 units. When the sex cells unite, the first generation hybrid will have the gene-composition:

A	a	d	D	H	h	k	K
b	B	E	e	i	I	L	l
C	c	f	F	J	j	m	M

This hypothetical hybrid will be 24 units in height, and will show considerable hybrid vigour. If this first generation is self-fertilised there will be a randomised shuffling and redistribution of chromosomes and the next generation will contain only 6.25 per cent of plants 24 units in height. The remaining 93.75 per cent of the plants will be less than 24 units in height, and will show little or no hybrid vigour. In other words, the optimum combination of favourable genes (in which a is masked by A, b by B, c by C, and so on), which was present in every individual in the first generation, occurs in only 6.25 plants out of every 100 in the second generation. To the observer who looks over the crop as a whole, hybrid vigour will appear to have vanished.

Jones' hypothesis, which provides for a unique combination of favourable genes in the first generation, explains why hybrid vigour decreases sharply in all generations after the first, and cannot be fixed; for the assumption that size is determined by genes on only four chromosomes is, of course, far too simple. If (as is more likely) genes on all chromosomes contribute to size determination, then in a plant like tobacco, which has 24 pairs of chromosomes, hybrid vigour in the second generation might appear in no more than one in 17 million individuals. Only a chronic optimist would expect to find this one plant; for all practical purposes hybrid vigour is never recovered after the first generation.*

Jones' hypothesis provides a formal explanation of hybrid vigour, but it still leaves plenty of opportunity for research and discussion. In particular neither the facts as we know them, nor the hypothesis in its present form, enable us to decide between three quite different interpretations of hybrid vigour. The first interpretation is that originally advanced by Jones, namely that hybrid vigour is something above the average, a biological bonus, as it were, due to the unique combination in the first generation of dominant linked genes favourable to development, some derived from the male parent and some from the female. The second interpretation is one developed recently by Jones, namely that *genes* degenerate when plants are inbred for many generations. They undergo changes into less efficient types of gene which are recessive and which become a drag on development; so an inbred line becomes progressively poorer and weaker. If a degenerate line is now crossed with some dissimilar line (perhaps also degenerate) the recessive degenerate genes in each line are masked by dominants from the other line, and the original normal vigour is restored. On this view, hybrid vigour is not anything supernormal: it is rather the degenerate parents which are sub-normal. Some support is given to this view by the fact that hybrid vigour is not nearly so common among wild plants as among cultivated plants, which have been isolated and allowed (on the criteria of natural selection) to degenerate. The third interpretation of hybrid vigour, proposed by another American worker, E. M. East, is that the vigour of hybrids is due to the fact that they are heterozygous:

*Recently, complex methods of maize breeding have been developed in the U.S.A. which apparently succeed in preserving some hybrid vigour through several generations.

some process occurs (not understood) whereby the effect on the plant of a gene *A* on one chromosome is intensified by the presence of its allele *a* on the partner chromosome. The gene *A* is stimulated by *a*, but not by another *A*, so that the gene-combination *Aa* has a greater influence on size than *AA* or *aa* have. East suggested that the two alleles might affect different, though related, processes in development. Some geneticists think that this is only a more sophisticated way of saying that hybrid vigour is due to the stimulus of a union between dissimilar sex cells. But it has one attraction: that it does not require the awkward assumption that genes favourable to growth should be dominant and unfavourable genes should be recessive.

A good deal more research is needed before we can decide whether one or other of these three interpretations accurately describes the genetics of hybrid vigour. Meanwhile recent experiments complicate rather than simplify the problem. For instance Powers in America has recently shown how it is possible to have hybrid vigour in fruit yield of tomatoes, even though genes for *small* size of fruit are partially dominant over genes for large size, and genes for *small* numbers of fruit are partially dominant over genes for large numbers. In other words, hybrid vigour may occur in organs for which favourable growth genes are not dominant. This contradictory result arises because yield depends on fruit size *multiplied* by fruit number: one growth process modifies another. We can illustrate how this might occur by reverting to the simplified example of the inheritance of plant height on page 13. It would be quite plausible to obtain such a result as the following:

	No. nodes	Internode length.	Total height.
PARENT 1	10	2	20
PARENT 2	2	10	20
Mean of parents	6	6	
F₁ HYBRID	5	5	25

The first generation hybrid has less than the mean number of nodes, and less than the mean internode length; in other words there is a partial dominance of the lower node number and the lower internode length; and yet there is hybrid vigour. Data such as these have been obtained for the yield of tomato fruits. They have to be treated with great caution, for reasons which will appear in the next section; but they are interesting, because they show in a simple way that it is not even necessary to assume that genes favourable to development are dominant; even without this assumption one can still produce a formal genetical explanation of hybrid vigour.

A Digression on the Physiology of Growth

From the geneticist's viewpoint hybrid vigour may be explained as luxuriant development in the first generation from a cross between dissimilar parents, due to a unique combination of favourable dominant genes; or (it amounts to the same thing) due to a unique suppression of degenerate recessive genes. And it is not difficult to give a formal explanation, by juggling with some symbols, of why hybrid vigour vanishes in the second generation. But these some-what arid theories do not help us much to understand what causes a hybrid to be larger; they are no more illuminating than the explanation that an archdeacon is a man who per-forms archidiaconal functions. For a clearer understanding of hybrid vigour we have to turn to the plant physiologist, and to ask first of all what factors determine size in plants, and secondly how these factors contrive to make some hybrids larger than their parents.

We have to begin with a slight digression on the physi-ology of growth. Consider what determines the size of a plant. A plant is made up of cells and its size depends there-fore on the number of cells and the size of the cells. Even for the simplest flowering plant it is impossible to count the one or to measure the other; but we can get an approximate measure of size from the weight of the plant, and the rate of

increase in weight is a tolerably good approximation to the
rate of increase in size. During the early stages of growth
of a plant the weight increases as though it were being added
at continuous compound interest. This is not surprising
when it is considered that one cell division begets two
daughter cells, and successive divisions of these two cells
give 4, 8, 16, 32, 64, 128, 256, 512, 1,024, etc. cells. As the
plant grows older, the rate of interest with which new tissues
are added decreases, and finally, at senescence, the rate falls
to zero.

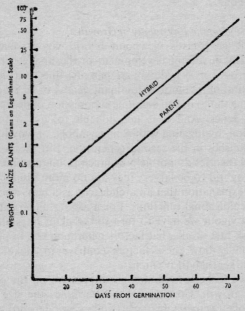

Fig. 1

Growth curves of a hybrid strain of maize and one of its parents.
Logarithms of weight are plotted against time from germination. On
this scale the slopes of the lines represent the relative growth rates
of the plant (*i.e.* the rate of interest at which cells are multiplying).

It is possible to use this similarity of growth and compound interest in the analysis of size in plants. For just as the size of a savings account depends on the capital invested and the rate of interest, so the size of a plant depends on the initial capital of dividing cells and their subsequent rate of division and growth. We may hazard the suggestion, therefore, that hybrid vigour in a plant is due to its possession of a faster growth rate and/or a larger capital of dividing cells than occur in the parent plants.

The Physiological Interpretation of Hybrid Vigour

Up to 1930 it was assumed that hybrid vigour was due simply to the fact that the hybrid grew faster, assimilated foodstuffs faster, and respired faster, than either of its parents. Every process in the hybrid was assumed to be speeded up. In that year a paper was published in which it was shown that for one maize hybrid (the hybrid illustrated in Plate 1) this is not correct: for, over the early period of growth from the seedling stage to the onset of flowering the hybrid grew at exactly the same rate of interest as one of its parents, no faster; and yet at the end of the experiment it was about nine times heavier than this parent. This puzzling result is illustrated in Figure 1, where the weights of the hybrid and one parent, from week to week, are plotted against time. The weights are plotted on a logarithmic scale because this brings into prominence the slope of the growth curves, which are a measure of the rates of interest.*

Let us return to the analogy of the savings account. If two savings accounts (both having had the same rate of interest for the same number of years) stand at £900 and £100, there is only one possible explanation for the difference, namely that more capital was invested in the first account than in the second. Similarly the explanation for the size of the

*When an organism is growing according to the compound-interest rule its average growth should be expressed on a logarithmic scale, because the ordinary linear scale is, so to speak, distorted. This is the reason why the figures quoted by Powers, above, which are not logarithmic averages, must be regarded with caution.

hybrid maize plant in Plate 1 must be sought in some initial advantage before the plant was twenty-one days old (when the first samples were taken). And indeed that is where the explanation for the size of this particular hybrid of maize was found: when the seed was dissected it was found that those parts of the embryo which grow into root and shoot were, in the hybrid, more massive than the corresponding parts in the parents. In this instance, therefore, the advantage in size of the hybrid was already present in the resting seed. This means, of course, that the hybrid embryo must have grown larger than the embryos of the inbred parents from which it came; in other words, hybrid vigour is determined very early in the life of the plant, even before germination.

A few years ago an English worker, Hatcher, carried out the difficult experiment of measuring the growth rates of embryos prior to the ripening of seed, and he found that under some circumstances the hybrid embryos do grow abnormally large.

Since 1930 a good deal of work has been done on the physiology of hybrid vigour. No clear-cut and simple conclusions emerge from this work. It is evident that among different crosses hybrid vigour is due to different causes. The principal causes, and some comments on their occurrence, are set out in the following paragraphs:

(a) Embryos in hybrid seed may be larger than embryos in parent seed. This is a common cause of hybrid vigour. It has been found in maize, tomato, and tobacco among plants and (if birth weight is substituted for embryo weight) in guinea pigs, pigs, rabbits, and mice among animals. But this is not the sole cause of hybrid vigour: larger embryos do not always grow into larger plants, and hybrid vigour may occur in plants whose embryos are not abnormally large. This inconsistency between initial biological capital and the size of the adult plant is due to a very interesting fact, namely that embryo size is determined not only by the gene-constitution of the embryo itself, but also by the gene-constitution of the mother; for the size of the embryo depends also on the size of the ovary and its nutrition; and these depend on the mother's genes. Now the probable state of affairs is this: that if an embryo is large because it carries genes for largeness, then it will grow into a large plant; but if an embryo is large because its maternal environment has been favourable to largeness, then the large embryo will produce only a normal plant. Hatcher reports an interesting example of this. He found that the size of seed (and embryo) in tomatoes depends on how many seeds there are in the fruit; the fewer seeds there are, the bigger they are. But largeness due to this cause does not persist as the plant grows, and (apart from making the analysis difficult) it has no relation to the largeness in embryos which leads to hybrid vigour.

(b) Hybrids may grow faster than their parents in the first few days after germination. This is a second contributory cause to hybrid vigour.

(c) One might expect the main contribution to the greater size of the hybrid to be made during the period of rapid growth which follows germination. It is therefore, a surprise to find that during this period, when the biological rate of interest is approximately constant, the hybrid grows at the same rate as one, or as both, of its parents. This has been found in several crosses both of plants and animals. There does not seem to be any well documented evidence that hybrid vigour is caused by greater growth in this period.

(d) As an annual plant approaches maturity its growth rate falls and eventually it stops growing altogether. In some hybrids, which display their vigour late in their life cycle, this waning of the growth rate is postponed, so that growth continues in the hybrid longer than in its parents. Some crosses between tall and dwarf varieties of tomatoes owe part of their vigour to this cause.

The geneticist interprets these various physiological causes of hybrid vigour as being due to genes which come into operation at various periods in the plant's life cycle.

One set of genes affects embryo growth rate; another set affects early growth; another set affects the time of onset of senescence. We do not understand why the genes which act very early in the life cycle and those which act very late have a more important effect upon the size of hybrids than genes which act in the intervening period. That is a topic for future research.

Size may be conveniently regarded as the result of a biological capital of active cells growing according to the laws of compound interest. How is this interest added ? Is a hybrid plant bigger than its parents because it has more cells or because its cells are larger ? All the evidence indicates that greater cell number and not greater cell size makes the hybrid bigger. The genes must act, therefore, to stimulate cell division and not simply cell expansion. Cell division requires energy and raw materials, both of which come from sugars. But, so far as our meagre evidence goes, plants which show hybrid vigour do not manufacture sugars any faster (relative to their size) than their parents, nor do they produce energy any faster. The old notion that hybrid vigour is accompanied by a 'speeding up' of all processes in the plant is incorrect in the few cases which have been studied. There is, however, interesting evidence that cell division is stimulated because the hybrid tissue is more efficient at cell chemistry than the tissues of either of its parents. For instance, extracts from hybrid maize grains stimulate the growth of the fungus *Ashbya Gossypii* more than extracts from inbred maize grains, which indicates that growth-promoting substances may be present in the hybrid maize in greater concentration than in its parents. More interesting still, Robbins in America has recently shown that roots of inbred and hybrid tomatoes, cut off and grown by themselves in tissue culture, behave differently toward certain growth substances; and roots of a hybrid are apparently able to synthesise pyridoxine and nicotinamide better than the roots of its parents.

This brings us up to the front line, as it were, of research on hybrid vigour. There is a plausible, but by no means proven genetical theory of hybrid vigour. There are some, but not nearly enough, data on the physiology of hybrid vigour. There is some promise, but not much more than promise, that further work will show hybrids to possess greater versatility and efficiency in their cell chemistry than their parents possess. There is opportunity for years of research in these fields. Meanwhile, hybrid vigour has an important part to play in agriculture. Through its careful exploitation, the farmer can make a substantial contribution to the world's clothes and the world's food.

SUGGESTIONS FOR FURTHER READING

EARLY WORK ON HYBRID VIGOUR.

Darwin, C., *The effects of cross and self fertilisation in the vegetable kingdom.* London 1876.

East, E. M., and Jones, D. F., *Inbreeding and Outbreeding.* Philadelphia, 1919. Chapters VII and VIII.

SUMMARY OF RECENT WORK WITH FULL BIBLIOGRAPHY.

Whaley, W. G., *Heterosis.* An article in the Botanical Review, Vol. X, 1944, pp. 461-498.

THE USE OF HYBRID VIGOUR IN AGRICULTURE.

Ashton, T., *The use of heterosis in the production of agricultural and horticultural crops.* The Imperial Bureau of Plant Breeding and Genetics, Cambridge, 1946.

Are Statistics Really Vital?

R. B. FISHER

It is usual to preface a work of fiction by a disclaimer of any sub-stance in the characters. The examples in this article are as much fiction as any fiction ever is, and the author would prefer his readers to go elsewhere for any authoritative information on the measurement of star positions, the germination of wheat, the diagnosis of jaundice, the genesis of epidemics, or on any of the other topics which have been introduced to illustrate statistical principles and methods. The example of coin-tossing is the only one drawn wholly from life.

THE answer is emphatically yes. In every field of human activity which depends on the interpretation of quantitive measurements, statistical analysis of the measurements plays a vital rôle. Research in any field of astronomy, economics or quantitative biology, or into the effectiveness of weapons of war, would be highly inefficient without the aid of stat-istical methods. Modern methods of industrial production control and all types of social and agricultural survey depend for their success on the application of statistical principles. These fields of activity form a small fraction of those in which statistical methods are essential for the effective use of available data, but they serve to exemplify the breadth of application of such methods.

How are statistical methods vital? This question is more difficult to answer than the first one. The aim of this article is to describe briefly the scope and importance of the statisti-cal methods most used in biological research. But in order to give some sort of answer to this second question it may be useful to anticipate a little at this point, and to indicate here by means of an example one of the most frequently met difficulties of all quantitative investigations and the part played by statistical methods in helping to overcome it.

Everyone has looked through the hot air rising from a car

radiator or from the embers of a bonfire and seen the land-
scape quivering. Just this type of apparent movement of
objects viewed through the atmosphere affects all the
measurements of star positions made by the astronomers,
since masses of hotter and colder air are continually being
churned together in the atmosphere through which the
astronomers must look at the stars. Thus a set of successive
measurements of the position of a star is bound to exhibit
irregular variations. Nothing the astronomer can do will
abolish this source of uncertainty in his measurements, so
that, if he is to use them, he must know just what degree of
reliability he can place on the average of any set of them, or,
conversely, how many measurements he must make in order
to attain a given degree of reliability.

Now in making experiments the work will be of little or
no value if all that the experimenter can say at the end of it
is: 'I found so and so, but I haven't the least idea if another
set of similar experiments would give the same answer or a
totally different one.' Unless an experimental investigation
is so designed, executed and analysed that a definite conclusion can be drawn concerning the outcome of any future
repetition of the investigation, the investigation will have
been a waste of time. Since in all experiments there are
factors outside the experimenter's control which affect the
measurements in the same way that the turbulent atmosphere affects the astronomer's measurements of star
positions, there is always some uncertainty concerning the
probable outcome of the repetition of any set of experiments. Statistical methods not only give the experimenter
ways of estimating the most probable outcome of any
future similar experiments, but also ways of putting limits
on his uncertainty, that is, of providing limits outside which
it is unlikely that the answers to any future sets of experiments could lie.

A great obstacle to the discussion of the proper rôle of
statistics in biology is the word 'statistics' itself. From the
original meaning of the study of populations there has

sprung such a family of inbred descendants that it is difficult
to disentangle their relationships. At the present time there
are three main meanings of the word, all relevant to the
present topic. The meaning most closely related to the
original is *the methods used for the study of collections of
quantitative data*. The second, an illegitimate but flourishing
and thrusting descendant of the first, is *any collection of
quantitative data*. The third, whose precise descent is difficult to trace, is *the quantitative measures which can be used to
characterise any group of quantitative data*.

A tabulation of the heights of a number of army recruits is
a collection of statistics (*second meaning*). Application of the
simpler methods of statistics (*first meaning*) to these data
will give the average height (which statisticians call the
mean height) and what is called the variance, a measure of
the scatter of the individual heights around the mean height.
These two quantities, the mean and the variance, are statistics
(*third meaning*).

We shall avoid this confusion by replacing the first meaning by *statistical methods* and the second by *data* or
quantitative data, reserving *statistics* for the third meaning
if we have occasion to use it. But we shall not be at the end
of confusion at this point. The scope of statistical methods
has been very differently understood by different workers,
so much so that as long ago as 1935 it was possible to list
more than a hundred definitions of the scope of statistical
methods. There is no point in adding to this plethora of
definitions. It is better to pass directly to an outline of the
types of statistical method available and their applicability
to biological problems.

All measurement can be regarded as consisting of a characteristic and a variable component. In the simplest instance
of measurement of a length the variable component is introduced by the uncertainty concerning the coincidence of
scale divisions with the ends of the line being measured. The
example of measurement of star positions provides a rather
more complicated instance. More complicated instances still

arise in the measurement of biological characteristics. Suppose that on a given day fifty years ago the heights had been measured of all boys in this country having their tenth birthdays on that day, and that similar measurements had been made this year. The mean heights of these two groups would provide the basis for a factual statement, which might well be that the average height of boys of 10 years was one inch greater in 1947 than in 1897. One might feel inclined to say that the average height of 10-year-old boys had increased by one inch in the fifty-year interval, and one could do so, provided it was made quite clear that this does not necessarily mean that 10-year-old boys in general are taller now than they were in 1897. We cannot interpret the change in mean until we have examined the type of scatter of the individual heights around the mean, that is what the statistician describes as the *frequency distribution of heights*.

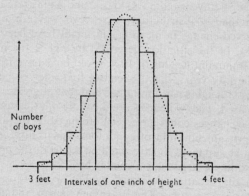

Fig. 1

The concept of frequency distribution is illustrated in Fig. 1. Let us suppose, quite arbitrarily, that the 10-year-old boys have heights ranging from three feet to four feet. We can then sort them into twelve groups according to height, the first containing all boys with heights from 3' 0'' to 3' 0¾'' (if heights are measured to the nearest ¼''), the second all

boys with heights from 3′ 1″ to 3′ 1¾″, and so on. If now we
make a diagram on squared paper, marking off horizontally
equal intervals corresponding to inches of height, and erect
on each interval a rectangle whose vertical length is proportional to the number of boys having heights falling in that
interval, we shall have a *histogram* or frequency distribution
diagram. If we had a very large number of boys and could
use much smaller intervals of height for our groups, so that
the histogram consisted of a very large number of very thin
rectangles, we could replace the histogram by a continuous
curve drawn through the mid-points of the tops of the rectangles, as is indicated by the dotted line in Fig. 1. Provided
that the relation of such curves to histograms is kept in
mind the curves are easier to use to illustrate distribution
problems than are the histograms themselves.

Reverting now to the interpretation of the change in mean
height of 10-year-old boys, Figs. 2 and 3 illustrate by means
of frequency distribution curves two ways in which the
observed change in mean height might have been brought
about. In the situation described by Fig. 2 the maximum
and minimum heights of 10-year-old boys have not altered
in the fifty years, but the relative frequency of occurrence
of lesser heights has diminished and that of greater ones has
increased. The two curves are therefore not the same shape.
These changes could have been produced by the disappearance or amelioration of conditions which, fifty years ago,
must be supposed to have acted on a part of the population
to produce a large class of stunted boys.

In the situation described by Fig. 3 the form of both
curves is the same. The maximum, mean and minimum
heights have all shifted upwards to the same extent. The
close similarity in form of the two curves may be taken to
mean that the variable component of the height has not
altered detectably, so that the change in mean height must
be ascribed to a change in the characteristic component of
the measurement. That is, in the situation described by
Fig. 3 one would feel confident that some systematic factor

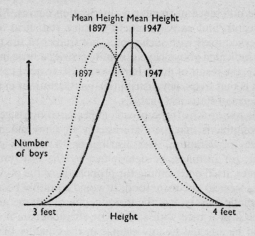

Fig. 2

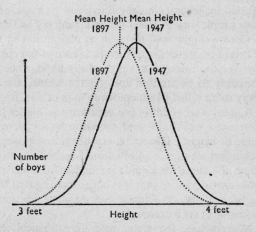

Fig. 3

operating on the whole population was responsible for the increase in height.

It is not profitable to pursue this point of the significance of the difference in frequency distribution curves. Much of nineteenth and early twentieth century statistical analysis concerned itself with such topics, but studies of the type we have indicated above have generally provided little information as the result of much hard work. All we need to keep in mind is that frequency distribution considerations enter into any form of statistical analysis.

The reason why the approach indicated above is generally unprofitable is that there are usually so many independent sources of variation. The distribution of heights of boys might, for instance, be determined by the distribution of incomes, itself determining the proportion of the population with access to adequate food. It would certainly be affected by genetic factors, e.g. the introduction of a large group of refugees of a race with a different characteristic height. It would be affected by any change in the equality of opportunity for adequate light, air and exercise. It would be affected by general changes in hygienic practice, and in a far from simple way. A lower general incidence of the taxations of disease might tend to result in diminution in variability of height owing to diminished incidence of the chance stuntings due to disease, but, on the other hand, since weaklings are likely to be stunted and, on the whole, are also more likely to be killed by an epidemic than others, improvement in hygiene may result in preservation of a higher proportion of stunted weaklings, and therefore in an increase in the range of heights. Dissection out of the components of such a complex set of causes of variation with no more than the shape of a curve for a guide is a matter for a seer rather than for a statistician, so that it is not surprising that the increasing objectivity of science has resulted in the fall into disfavour of such exercises.

Nevertheless, the great need for statistical methods in biology arises out of the large effects of multifarious uncontrollable sources of variation such as those discussed above. In fact, the magnitude of the resultant variation is commonly so large in biological instances that it has been exalted, quite

unnecessarily, into a specific concept of 'biological variation.' In the two examples given below the most important
source of variation is the same in each instance although the
first example is of a physical experiment and the second
of a biological one. Consider first the number of times a
coin turns up heads in a group of twenty trials. In any one
trial heads may appear any number of times from 0 to 20,
although we can confidently predict that the most probable
number of heads in a group of twenty trials will be 10, if the
coin be perfectly formed, and that the mean number of
heads per twenty trials will approach closer and closer to 10
as we increase the number of groups of twenty trials. If we
were investigating the coin to determine whether it was
biassed we should want to know, in effect, whether the
mean number of heads per group of twenty trials gradually
approached 10 as the number of groups of trials increased,
or became stable at some other number.

Now consider, for the second example, the following
problem. We have a supply of a variety of wheat and we
wish to know what proportion of the grains will germinate
in given conditions. We may attempt to cause all the grains
to germinate, which will effectively prevent us from making
other parallel or subsequent observations on this type of
grain, or we may take a number of small samples, determine
the proportion germinating in each, and estimate from these
data what limiting percentage germinating we should have
found if we had taken bigger and bigger samples, culminat-
ing in the whole available supply.

In both these examples we are dealing with a source of
variation described as *sampling variation*. When we take a
handful of wheat grains we may by chance include in it a
higher proportion of seeds capable of germinating than
there is in the whole supply. But we are equally likely to take
a sample containing a lower proportion than exists in the
whole supply. Our problem is that we can measure the
sample taken, but usually, as in the case of coin-tossing, we
cannot measure the whole supply from which the sample is

taken. Nevertheless, what we are really interested in is the
characteristics of the whole supply, or, as the statistician
would put it, in the characteristics of the *population* from
which the samples of data were drawn. The only way of
getting an estimate of the characteristics of the population
is to find out by statistical methods what theoretical populations could have yielded the observed samples. This is a
difficult concept, and we may illustrate it with the example
of germinating wheat. We may suppose that, out of 10
samples of 100 grains, treated similarly, we observe that
70, 71, 71, 73, 73, 73, 76, 77, 77 and 81 germinate respectively, the mean number germinating per sample of 100
being 74.2. We can then say, after we have made the necessary computations, that there is less than one chance in a
hundred of obtaining such a set of samples as those
observed, from any population of seeds in which the per-
centages capable of germinating lay outside the limits of
71.1 and 77.3. If we needed to fix the germination characteristics of this variety of wheat with greater certainty we
should have to examine a larger number of samples.

It is particularly important to note that sampling variation is inherent in all experimental work, and that no
conclusions dependent on the magnitude of any quantitative
characteristic of a sample can be safely drawn unless some
process analogous to that above has been carried out. The
proposition is practically self-evident that, since you cannot
escape the operations of sampling variation, you cannot
avoid the necessity for statistical analysis in any experimental study.

A first extension of the sort of procedure just described
can be illustrated by considering the measurements of the
resting blood pressure of a group of fifty young men of 20
years of age. We compute the mean blood pressure and the
variance of the observed values, the variance being a
measure of scatter of values around the mean. From the
variance and the number of observations we can compute a
third statistic, *the variance of the mean*, which is a measure

of the expected scatter of means of other samples. If the
mean is 120 mm. of mercury and the variance is such that
there is only one chance in a hundred of finding an individual
blood pressure outside the range of 90–150 mm. mercury,
then the variance of the mean will be such that there will be
only one chance in a hundred of obtaining a mean outside
the limits of 116–124 mm. mercury in another similar
sample. So far we have done no more than in the germinating wheat example. But now consider a corresponding
sample of young women of the same age, with a mean blood
pressure of 110 mm. mercury and the same variance and
variance of mean. There is then only one chance in a hundred of obtaining a second sample of such young women in
which the observed mean is outside the limits of 106–114.
If we now consider pairs of samples of fifty, one each of
each sex, in only one out of 100×100 of such pairs will the
means of both groups be outside the stated limits, and in
only one quarter of such rare instances will the female mean
be above 114 at the same time that the male mean is below
116. Thus the chance of ever observing a mean female blood
pressure in this age group which exceeds a mean male one
is so small as to be quite negligible. There need be no reasonable doubt that the female data are drawn from a different
population in the statistical sense from that yielding the
male data. Put yet another way, we can state confidently
that there is a systematic sex difference in blood pressure at
this age, and our confidence will not be shaken by the fact
that in any two groups taken for measurement there will
undoubtedly be a considerable number of females whose
blood pressures are higher than those of a considerable
number of the males.

This sort of comparison of the means of two samples of
observations is of very wide application in experimental
science and in other fields, and there are many extensions
and elaborations of it. If, for instance, we have observations
on the yield of wheat per acre of a particular area in successive years, and we also have data for mean rainfall, we could

classify the years into those of lower rainfall, i.e. from zero
up to the mean annual rainfall observed, and those of higher
rainfall, i.e. in excess of the observed mean, and we could
investigate whether the mean yields from these two groups
of years could or could not have been drawn from the same
population. If they could not be so drawn with any appreciable probability we can conclude that rainfall has a systematic effect on yield. Alternatively, we can regard the yield
in any one year as made up of a characteristic part, determined by the variety of wheat and the type of soil, a variable
part determined by rainfall, and a residual variable part
determined by all the other possible factors such as incidence
of pests, frosts, sunlight. We can then use the technique of
regression analysis to determine to what extent we can
account for the variation in yield in terms of variation in
rainfall. At this point another tricky problem of exposition
presents itself. Just as it is always possible to draw a straight
line through any two points, so it is always possible to draw
a curve, if it is of a sufficiently complicated character,
through any given number of scattered points on a graph.
So we could, if we wished, always account for the whole
yield in terms of rainfall if we chose a sufficiently complicated form of relationship between the two, but it would
gain us nothing, because nothing could be more certain than
that the next point we obtained would require another
increase in the complexity of our relationship, and our curve
would be of no possible use except as a pretentious and
cumbrous description of the points themselves. What we do
when we perform a regression analysis is to set up some
hypothesis concerning the nature of the relation between
rainfall and yield, and then fit the best curve of the general
character required by the hypothesis, the best curve being
that which accounts for the largest part of the variation in
yield in terms of variation in rainfall. The simplest hypothesis to test would be that the yield consisted of a characteristic portion plus a portion directly proportional to rainfall,
that is, in mathematical terms,

$$y = ar + b,$$

where y is yield, r is rainfall and a and b are constants. Since this equation is represented graphically by a straight line, this type of regression hypothesis is called a *linear regression*. However, it is much more likely that the yield will be very low for low rainfalls, pick up sharply for moderate ones, improve less and less as the rainfall gets heavier, and probably begin to fall off quite seriously as it approaches torrential. Such a type of relation can be most simply described by a curve corresponding to such an equation as—

$$y = a + br + cr^2 + dr^3,$$

c and d being new constants capable of taking negative values when necessary, the other symbols having the same meaning as before. The regression analysis consists in finding the values of the constants a, b, c, d, which account for the maximum possible part of the variation in yield in terms of rainfall. Then, in a fashion entirely analogous to what has gone before, the variance of these constants is estimated.

When we have the value and the variance of a regression constant, we can determine the probability of obtaining the observed constant from a population of regression constants with the same variance, but with a mean of zero. If, for instance, this probability is very high for b in the first equation above, we conclude that we could readily by chance obtain the observed small apparent dependence of yield on rainfall in the absence of any real relation between the two, and we say that no dependence of yield on rainfall can be established. By the same sort of procedure, applied to the second equation, we can see whether we can establish a dependence of yield on the square or cube of the rainfall, and if, in statistical parlance, any of the coefficients b, c or d proves to be 'not significantly different from zero' we amend our hypothesis by omitting the corresponding term from our equation and obtaining better estimates for the coefficients of the other terms.

Other sorts of curves can be used, so that we can use regression analysis to test whether the relation between two

variables conforms reasonably to any one of a wide variety
of theoretical relations. But we always have to supply the
theoretical relations, and the answers always come out in
the form that the data are or are not consistent with the
hypothesis tested. That is, one can always demonstrate, in
the appropriate case, that the data are not consistent with a
particular hypothesis. But where the data fit the hypothesis
there is nothing to deny the possibility of their fitting
another hypothesis equally well or better. This is not a
defect of statistical analysis, but of the experimental method
itself. The outstanding benefit which good statistical ground-
ing confers on the experimentalist is that it prevents him
from falling into the error of supposing that if he feeds a set
of puzzling results into a statistician's calculating machine
the monster will tell him what they mean. The experimental
method, by virtue of the limitations imposed by sampling,
can never provide absolute proof of a quantitative hypothesis concerning a relation between variables. It can only
demonstrate that the observed variations in the one variable
can be or cannot be accounted for in at least one way in
terms of variations in the other.

An obvious and powerful extension of regression analysis
is to replace our second equation above by one of the form
of—

$$y = a + br + cs + dt,$$

where s and t are new variables, such, for instance as sun-
shine and temperature. We can no longer describe this
regression in terms of a curve. In fact, we should need a
four-dimensional figure if we wished to represent it geo-
metrically. But the same principles hold, and we again
estimate the values of the coefficients and their variances,
and determine which of them are 'significantly different
from zero'. Where a coefficient is not significantly different
from zero we say that we cannot establish any dependence of
yield on the corresponding variable. This type of analysis is
a *multiple regression analysis*.

In the multiple regression analysis we are assuming that

the variations in y can be separated into variations due to variations in r, s and t, together with residual variations due to unmeasured factors. This sort of *analysis of variance* has been very much refined and developed in recent years and now forms the most delicate and generally applicable of all statistical techniques, the major figure in the development being R. A. Fisher. The first developments were in connection with agricultural fertiliser trials, where one of the greatest bars to accurate comparison of effects lay in the gradients in soil fertility which have been frequently demonstrated. R. A. Fisher developed experimental lay-outs which permitted the subsequent use of analysis of variance to obtain the most accurate possible comparisons between treatments. A simple example is illustrated in Fig. 4. The large square represents a plot of land divided into sixteen small plots. The four letters A, B, C and D represent four treatments to which a crop sown over the whole area is to be subjected. It will be seen that, with the arrangement used, the following conditions are fulfilled :—

(i) each horizontal and vertical strip is divided equally between the four treatments, and

(ii) each treatment occurs once in each vertical and once in each horizontal strip.

B	C	A	D
A	D	B	C
D	A	C	B
C	B	D	A

Fig. 4—Design of the simplest type of agricultural field trial. For explanation of symbols see text.

Thus the sources of variance in the total yields of strips will be the variations in the properties of the soil from plot to plot, the effects of treatments being balanced out. If on the other hand we take the total yields of plots receiving the same treatment, here we shall have balanced out the shifts in soil fertility, since each row and column is represented in each treatment total, and the variance will be primarily due to difference in treatments. In each of these instances the variance will be increased by the inclusion of a fraction of the variance due to the essential variability of the crop. We can also obtain, by a method which is difficult to explain simply, a direct estimate from these same data of the magnitude of the variance due to the essential variability of the crop. It is unfortunate that this is difficult to explain, because this procedure of splitting up the variance into its components (in this instance into the components due to soil fertility differences, differences in treatments, and essential variability of the crop) is what gives the method of analysis its great power, and furnishes the experimental results with greater precision than can be obtained by any other method.

In this instance, if we can now show that the variance due to difference in treatments plus crop variability is greater than that due to crop variability alone, we can establish that the treatments have definitely affected the crop, and we can go further and establish which treatments have had an effect. Further, since we eliminate the effects of soil variability, we can set much closer limits to the probable treatment effects in any repetition than we could with any other procedure using the same number and size of plots.

The statistician is at this point invading the experimental field in another way. He is not only analysing the experimental results, he is designing the experiment. Although the subject is highly complicated and quite unsuited for detailed exposition in a short article, enough must be said about it to indicate the great importance of this development. The experimental designs which have evolved from such starting points as Fig. 4 now make it practicable to examine the effects of three or four different variables at once in such a way that the influence of each factor on the effects of the others can be sorted out from the data, as well as the effects of the individual factors. Whereas the labour of such a project would be prohibitive by any traditional method it is usually quite simple to set up an appropriate experimental design on the principles worked out by the statistical analysts, and it can be shown that such designs have a far smaller chance of giving misleading results than has the traditional procedure of varying one factor at once.

| | Order of Tests | | | | |
	I	II	III	IV	V
P	A.1	B.2	C.3	D.4	E.5
Q	B.3	C.4	D.5	E.1	A.2
Observers R	C.5	D.1	E.2	A.3	B.4
S	D.2	E.3	A.4	B.5	C.1
T	E.4	A.5	B.1	C.2	D.3

Fig. 5—Design of an experiment to test methods of haemoglobin determination. For explanation of symbols see text.

It should be pointed out, before leaving this topic, that designs similar to that of Fig. 4 are just as applicable to laboratory experiments as to field trials. Fig. 5 illustrates a design of an experiment for testing clinical methods of determining the hæmoglobin content of blood. The group of methods to be tested have the common feature that the hæmoglobin (the red pigment of blood) in a measured volume of blood is first converted chemically into a derivative whose colour is stable and then the sample of blood is progressively diluted until it matches the colour of a permanent colour standard. At one time it became uncomfortably clear that this comparison technique could give rise to large differences between different estimates of the hæmoglobin content of the sample of blood. The experiment of Fig. 5 is designed to test the suitability of different comparison procedures and different backgrounds against which to view the colours. We have five comparison procedures, designated A – E, and five backgrounds, 1 – 5, and we place these in the squares of our diagram. The five rows, P – T, represent the five observers, who are to make the tests and the five columns, I, II, III, IV, V, represent the order in which the tests are to be carried out. With this design requiring a total of twenty-five observations, we can sort out the effects of practice or fatigue (columns), differences between observers (rows), effects of procedures and of backgrounds, and effects of residual error (analogous to the essential variability of the crop in the previous example). In this instance the residual error will be due largely to errors in measuring the blood, in diluting, and in reading the final volume. Our final test of whether either of comparison procedures or backgrounds can be held accountable for the variability of the results will be much more sensitive than it would have been if every observer had tested every combination of background and procedure. We can be certain of getting at least as reliable an answer as we could have obtained from ten times as many observations made on the traditional plan. Another advantage of the newer designs is exemplified by this experiment. Most experimental material used in acute biological experiments changes fairly rapidly with time. Isolated animal and plant tissues gradually proceed to break-down and death. Biochemical preparations are always threatened by the invasion of bacteria and subsequent putrescence. Blood is no exception, and there is little doubt that in a traditional design of the hæmoglobin experiment, requiring some fifty observations on the part of each observer, the time required for the experiment would be such that the progressive change in the sample of blood used would introduce a new and important source of variation which would largely neutralise any advantage of the complete repetition of all the combinations of procedure and background by each observer. So we come back to the point that the newer designs are essential for the practical prosecution of large fields of experimental work.

There are numerous other aspects of statistical technique which are of biological and medical importance which cannot be adequately discussed in the small space remaining. The theory of *statistical estimation* is a fascinating and important technique, essential, for example, to the geneticist who requires to estimate linkage between genes from the results of breeding experiments. The technique of *discriminant functions* is a means of finding the best combination of two or more measurable attributes for the distinction of two sub-classes of a population. For instance, there are two types of jaundice which are difficult to distinguish. One calls for surgical treatment, the other for medical treatment. A large number of biochemical tests have been proposed for aiding diagnosis, four of which are generally used, and it can be shown by discriminant technique that a particular combination of two of these tests gives a better distinction than any other combination of any of the four. Since the combination gives a far less equivocal answer than any amount of contemplation of the individual test results from which the combination is derived, the discriminant technique here gives a greater certainty of diagnosis for far less laboratory work. Discriminant technique has been used for the classification of varieties of plant, insect, and fossil human species, for the detection of accident-prone workers, and for the selection of men likely to make good salesmen, for example.

The *analysis of time series* is another statistical technique which promises much in the study of epidemiological problems and in the study of animal and plant populations. This type of technique owes much to the economists, and deals with the type of problem in which the value of a variable at any one time is largely affected, though not necessarily simply, by the values it possessed at earlier times. An epidemic outbreak of a disease may, for instance, leave behind it a large number of people who have had very mild undetected attacks and who have acquired immunity. It may also leave behind it a smaller number of people harbouring the causative organism because they possess enough resistance to prevent it multiplying freely within them but not enough to destroy it rapidly. Both this 'carrier' state and the immunity may disappear with time. If the carriers remain carriers for longer than the immune class remain immune, there may be another epidemic outbreak when the immune class has shrunk sufficiently. But the occurrence or non-occurrence of this epidemic will probably depend on whether the immunologically favourable conditions occur at a favourable time of year, e.g. in the fly-ridden months if the organism is spread from the carriers by flies. Thus if, as is quite possible, the duration of immunity depended on the severity of the epidemic in which it was acquired, a mild epidemic might be followed by disappearance of immunity too early in the year for carriers to be dangerous, a moderate epidemic might produce optimal conditions for a subsequent heavy epidemic, and a heavy epidemic might result in immunity being prolonged in the following year throughout the period of danger from carriers. Thus, although, in this hypothetical instance, there would undoubtedly be a set of relations between severities of incidence in successive years, the relations would be of a complex kind, even if such important accessory factors as variations in fly population did not increase their complexity. The necessary techniques for disclosing these relations are correspondingly complex, and the interpretation of the results is still a matter of some controversy.

Other techniques derived from such widely separated fields as psychology on the one hand and the actuarial offices of insurance companies on the other have found applications in the biological field, but their applications are too restricted to make it profitable to discuss them here.

The best test of the success of this article will be whether at this point the reader will agree that it is obvious that statistical analysis is an essential part of all experimental research. Sampling variation is always present in any experimental situation, and only in a small fraction of the simplest situations, where one variable only is altered, and where alteration of it produces variations which are very large compared with those produced by all other factors, can one replace the formal statistical analysis by the informal one which one performs whenever one examines a collection of figures.

Whenever the experimenter is faced with the necessity to alter more than one variable at once, as for instance, in feeding experiments in animals, where the animal is growing the whole time, so that time and diet are the minimum variables, there can be no doubt that the interpretation of the experimental results can only be made reliably on the basis of statistical analysis. Further, some of the most profitable types of experimental investigation can be carried out only if the experiment is designed on statistical principles, and some types of experimental enquiry, such as the example of the best way of distinguishing types of jaundice, are essentially statistical enquiries.

Lastly, and most importantly, the reader should have perceived that quantitative experimental work must always be directed to the objective of testing an hypothesis. One may collect a lot of figures "to see what they mean", but no amount of elaborate computation will reveal any hidden meaning until the investigator introduces a hypothesis concerning the meaning. He must start with some such hypothesis as that the mean of one series is greater than or not greater than that of another, or that the value of one variable is influenced in some specified general fashion by that of another, before he can obtain any answer at all. Thus, if the biologist without technical statistical training is to make use of the statistician without biological training, he must at least know enough of the scope and language of statistics to be able to state the hypothesis or hypotheses to be tested in terms which the statistician can understand. Statistical knowledge is, in fact, as essential a technical aid to any experimenter in quantitative biology as is a knowledge of radio amplifier technique to the experimental neurophysiologist. The ideal relation between the experimenter and the statistician would be that in which the experimenter was familiar with statistical principles and with standard techniques, so that he was independent of the statistician except for computation facilities and for advice on technical points and on problems lying near the growing points of statistical knowledge. In such a relation the experimenter would impose the minimum routine burden on the statistician, and at the same time be far more likely to focus the statistician's attention on those problems of statistical technique which are of direct practical value. The example of Rothamsted Experimental Station, where R. A. Fisher developed the analysis of variance methods in direct relation to the needs of agricultural field trials, is a magnificent advertisement for this type of relation.

The case for the introduction of elementary instruction in statistical principles into all experimental science courses is very strong, but I should like to go further. Statistical methods are now coming to play their proper part in almost every field of human endeavour in which measurements are made or examined. The fundamentals of these methods, and the principles underlying them, are basically simple, and could readily be acquired in the science side of the upper forms of secondary schools and their equivalents. I feel that they should be taught there as a matter of course. There are very few of us who are not faced with necessities to decide a course of action on a quantitative basis at some time or another, and such a training would inculcate a fundamentally sounder attitude to the quantitative aspects of life than is usually to be seen at present.

FURTHER READING

The treatment of clinical and laboratory data. By Donald Mainland (Oliver and Boyd). This is an admirably lucid account of the necessity for and technique of simple statistical analysis, with the minimum of mathematics.

Statistical analysis in biology. By K. Mather (Methuen). This book contains accounts of the principles and of many of the practical details of all the statistical methods likely to be directly useful to the experimental biologist. No mathematics beyond elementary algebra are required.

Statistical mathematics. By A. C. Aitken (Oliver and Boyd). This little book gives a very neat outline of the mathematical bases of statistical methods, but requires a fair knowledge of mathematics.

Statistical methods for research workers and *The design of experiments.* By R. A. Fisher (Oliver and Boyd). These are classical works, but they are far from easy. They would serve to enlarge an understanding of the subject gained from Mather's book recommended above.

The Insect Menace to Stored Products

BY JOHN A. FREEMAN

Photogravure illustrations between pp. 64 and 65

1. Introduction

MUCH more publicity is always given to outbreaks of pests which attack growing crops or cause diseases of man or animals, than to the steady loss which occurs from the depredations of the pests of stored products. Thus most people are aware of the losses caused to agriculture by the Colorado potato beetle, the codling moth and the locust; of the diseases carried by the malarial mosquito, the louse and the tsetse fly; but few are aware of the large quantities of food annually destroyed by the ravages of the grain weevil, the cacao moth and the flour mite.

Farmers and those who dwell in areas where insect-borne diseases are prevalent can see immediately the effects of insect attack. The farmer may suffer the loss of young turnips by flea beetle attack or see the whole of his crop of maize eaten by locusts; people in the tropics may fall victims to malaria or yellow fever. But it is often not until grain starts to get hot and large numbers of grains are found to have been consumed that the weevils are discovered. Much stored produce moves fairly rapidly from hand to hand in the course of trade and although the insects continue their attacks throughout the process the incidence of loss is gradual and it is not usually recognised unless the goods remain in store for some time undisturbed. The farmer cannot move his young plants from the ground if they are attacked by insects, but a merchant can readily sell

both grain and insects and thus pass on the liability for loss.
The consumer, of course, eventually bears the cost of that
which the insects have eaten. Connected with this aspect of
the problem is the fact that many of those responsible for
the storage and handling of products have not appreciated
the true nature of infestation by insects and mites, believing
it to be inevitable, an "inherent vice" of the commodity,
spontaneously generated within it and therefore not subject
to control.

It is one of the objects of this article to set out some of
the facts relating to the biology and control of stored
products pests and to show that their depredations are
avoidable and can be prevented by the proper application
of present knowledge.

2. *Loss and damage caused by insects and mites*
General

The estimation of losses caused by the attacks of pests of
stored products is very difficult and complex. The absolute
minimum loss may be measured by the amount of material
consumed by the insects, which should have been made use
of by man. But there are so many secondary results of the
direct attack which give rise to losses that a figure based on
this consideration alone is quite misleading. For example,
whereas one might estimate the loss in a bulk of wheat by
the difference in weight before and after storage (making due
allowance for alterations in water content), one cannot do
this for the damage effected by a moth caterpillar to a suit
of clothes. In the latter case several small holes render the
clothing unusable but the amount of material consumed is
negligible. Furthermore the criteria of assessing losses are
different in countries of highly developed civilisations from
those of primitive economy where the population always
lives near the famine line. If these factors are all taken into
consideration and the wide possibility of error in the various
estimates is granted, then the following figures may be taken
as examples.

Financial Estimates

It has been pointed out by Metcalf and Flint that 'the pests of stored products are the most expensive of all to feed, because they feed upon products which have been grown, harvested, stored and, in many cases, have incurred further expense through manufacturing, advertising, selling and distributing processes'.

In 1946 a conference of experts, convened in Washington by the United Nations Food and Agricultural Organisation, estimated that the overall annual loss to cereals and cereal products from the attacks of storage pests amounted to about 5% of the crops harvested. A great proportion of these crops is retained for consumption in the countries where they are grown and only a relatively small proportion enters into world trade. The overall losses due to attack by insects are equal to about one half of the total amount passing annually into world trade, i.e., if the losses due to storage pests could be prevented the quantities of grain available to deficiency areas which are unable to grow enough for themselves would be about doubled. The United States of America has a well organised service for the prevention of losses, both to the growing as well as the harvested crop, but for the year 1936 it was estimated that the total losses to stored products from the attacks of insects and mites amounted to some three hundred million dollars. Balzer estimated that the annual losses to the stored rice crop in the U.S.A. amounted to about three million dollars, about 10% of the value of the crop. This estimate was for direct losses and did not take into account any consequential damage. Under normal storage conditions in Malaya, Jack and Jagoe estimated that the storage life of rice was only eight months before it became unfit for human consumption. The losses to stored grain in India have been variously estimated as between $2\frac{1}{2}$ and 5% per annum. At 5% the actual quantity lost would be about $3\frac{1}{2}$ million tons; at the $2\frac{1}{2}$% rate the effect of the amount eaten by insects is the deprivation of four million people of their food for twelve months. It has been estimated that the quantity of stored grain destroyed annually in India by storage pests is approximately equal to the amount imported during the same period. In the tobacco trade in the United Kingdom, the attacks of the cacao or tobacco moth (*Ephestia elutella*) on stored tobacco in 1929, resulted in losses of some £100,000. In Germany it has been estimated that in a typical pre-war year the annual damage caused by the clothes moth in households amounted to 60 million Reichsmarks. Insects which attack animal products such as hides also cause severe losses. In the U.S.A. such damage caused by the copra beetle (*Necrobia rufipes*) and the cheese skipper fly (*Piophila casei*) has been estimated at 1.2 million dollars a year. Considerable damage too is caused to the structure of buildings and to furniture by wood-boring beetles. Fortunately the termite does not breed in our climate, but the powder-post beetle and the furniture beetle cause annually considerable losses.

The kinds of damage

These may be dealt with under three headings. *Firstly*, there is the direct loss of material actually consumed by the insects and thereby lost to human use; *secondly*, there is the loss of material contaminated or otherwise fouled by insect attack; and *thirdly*, there is the loss of trade, goodwill and business reputation arising from the sale of infested goods.

Direct losses are the most important where large quantities of stored produce have to be stored for long periods under conditions favourable to the multiplication of insects. During the 1914–1918 war large quantities of wheat were stored in vast bagged dumps in Australia and heavy losses resulted from the attacks of grain insects. In one yard alone up to one ton of weevils was swept up and destroyed every day. Eventually the cost of control operations and the direct and indirect losses caused by the insects amounted to over £1,000,000. Much grain which is imported into the

United Kingdom arrives already more or less damaged by grain-boring insects (Plate 2); food which should have been available for human beings and farm animals has already been eaten by insects. A similar, but slightly different type of loss occurs with oilseeds (Plate 3). There the effect of attack by insects is to cause loss of quantity and quality of the oil which may be so deteriorated that oilseeds intended for crushing to produce edible oil may have to be used in the manufacture of soap. Insects and mites may cause loss of germinative capacity in seed grain and malting barley by destroying the embryo of the grain.

Direct losses are greatest when commodities have to be held in store for long periods under unsuitable conditions or without adequate precautions against insect attack. This occurs when goods are held for an increase in price or when transport facilities are insufficient to move accumulated surpluses harvested at limited times of year.

Some secondary results of attack by insects may now be considered. The presence of large numbers of insects in bulk stored grain may cause the grain to get hot, even when the moisture is too low to permit heating due to mould attack or the respiration of the grain itself. It has been shown that heating can be started by quite small numbers of insects concentrated in a small area in the mass of bulk grain. As grain is a poor conductor, the heat produced by the insects is not dissipated as fast as it is produced and the temperature rises in the neighbourhood of the insects. This causes increased activity on the part of the insects. Eventually the temperature at the centre becomes too high for the free-living insects, which move outwards, but the grubs which are within the grains are killed. Finally the whole mass of grain becomes heated to a temperature of about 115 to 120 deg. F., and covered with a seething mass of adult insects. It may also be caked, mouldy and sprouting (Plate 8). The amount of grain actually consumed by the insects may be very small, but the grain may be musty and damaged in various ways which make it unsuitable for the manufacture of flour. Grain for germination (seed or malting), will almost certainly have been ruined.

Many insects produce objectionable silk webbing (Plate 5) and masses of excrement, in addition to the cast skins of larvæ, as they live in the food. Some insects and mites impart an objectionable odour to the food, even when they are present in quite small numbers. Thus the strong-smelling secretion produced by the flour mite will persist through to cooked products made from infested raw materials such as flour, pudding powders and custard powder. Flour beetles cause flour to have a sour taint and a yellow colour. As already mentioned the slight damage to clothing by the clothes moth may cause a garment to be discarded even though the actual quantity of material eaten is minimal. It is impossible to 'draw' on a cigar or cigarette which has a single exit hole of the tobacco beetle or has been damaged by the attacks of moths, although the quantity of tobacco eaten is negligible (Plate 6). Evidence of the presence of insects in the form of the insects themselves (living or dead), webbing and droppings is sufficient to induce many people to discard the whole packet of goods even though the amount of damage done by the insects is small and the contaminated material might be used for animal feeding or other industrial uses. In this matter the strict pure food laws in the U.S.A. annually result in the condemnation of quantities of foodstuffs in which pieces of insects or their droppings can be detected, even though no living insects are present. Rejection on these grounds, however, is generally so far confined to countries of highly organised civilisation and infested food has to be consumed in primitive countries, the insects being picked out in the course of preparation.

The *third* major category of loss may now be examined, i.e., loss of business goodwill and trade reputation. Where goods are sold under branded names, in particular, the discovery of insects in one line leads to loss of sale not only of that particular line, but also of all other lines of the same manufacturer, whether or not the other commodities are

liable to infestation. Quite apart from the hygienic aspect,
this is one of the reasons why the canners are chary of using
weevilly beans (Plate 7). In the same way the manufacturers
of chocolate and tobacco take considerable precautions to
prevent infestation of their finished products by insects
which enter the factory on the raw materials. The loss due
to the presence of one caterpillar in a box of cigarettes or a
box of chocolates is not confined to compensation for that
particular unit, but is liable to set the customer against the
whole range of the firm's goods or even that of the whole
industry. Trouble of this kind is not confined to infestible
commodities. High quality goods such as clothing and
canned goods may be infested, albeit superficially, by insects
left behind in railway vans or in lorries or ships after former
infested goods. The person handling the goods naturally
takes exception to the presence of insects and may reject the
whole consignment. Not infrequently it is the carrier who
suffers the immediate loss.

To sum up one may conclude that even in countries where
the climatic conditions are such that large-scale rapid destruction of food and other commodities by insects does not
occur and where organisations exist to control infestation,
nevertheless there are substantial losses. In countries where
the standard of storage of commodities is poor there are, on
the other hand, heavy direct losses although the secondary
losses are perhaps of less economic importance. The losses
in the retained stocks are, of course, of great importance in
the world economy since the smaller the losses in the
retained stocks the quicker can the standard of living be
raised in such countries and the surplus available for other
countries made all the greater.

3. Biology and ecology of stored products pests

The two groups of invertebrate animals which are responsible for the losses already described are insects (IN-
SECTA) and mites (ACARINA) which belong to the same
group, Arachnida, as spiders. Knowledge of their biology is

fundamental to the intelligent application of methods of prevention and control.

The insects and mites found in stored products are generally of small size (less than $\frac{1}{2}$ inch long) and inconspicuous. They tend to prefer dark parts and often remain hidden within the foodstuffs unless disturbed. When that occurs they will often leave the food and secrete themselves in crevices in the structure of the store.

Insects breathe air, which is conducted directly to the tissues through systems of branching tubes opening through "spiracles" at the sides of the body. Many mites breathe directly through the skin. It is possible for both, however, to reduce their rate of respiration considerably provided the external conditions permit. Excess of carbon dioxide in the air will cause the spiracles to remain open. This reaction has been made use of in fumigation by mixing carbon dioxide with the lethal fumigant gas. In normal practice it is common to use a mixture of carbon dioxide with ethylene oxide to reduce the danger of explosion and incidentally this precaution increases the efficiency of the fumigation by its effect on the physiology of the insect.

Insects and mites are principally affected by the temperature and humidity of the surrounding air. Generally there is an optimum combination of these factors for each stage of development of each species. Insects and mites tend to prefer conditions of relatively high humidity (say 60% relative humidity* and upwards). Both may be active over a wide range of temperature. Whilst the flour mite may continue to feed down to a few degrees above freezing point, most stored products insects show little activity at tempera-

*The most common method of expressing the amount of water vapour in the air is the "percentage relative humidity". This figure states the amount of water vapour in the air as a proportion of the amount which the air can hold. The actual quantity of water vapour required to saturate a given volume of air varies with the temperature, warm air holding more than cold air. Thus if unsaturated warm air is cooled the "relative humidity" will rise until the air is saturated (*i.e.* 100 per cent relative humidity), but the actual quantity of water remains unchanged.

tures below 50° F., and many pests of tropical origin will die if exposed for long to temperatures below 40° F. Whilst it is possible to kill some species and to inhibit the activity of most by keeping them at low temperatures, it is a difficult matter to kill some species in this way, since they can adapt themselves to resist freezing. At the other end of the scale activity increases to about 90° F., above which temperature conditions become increasingly adverse and all stages are killed by exposure to 140° F. for a few minutes.

Stored products insects and mites, like other animals, develop from eggs laid by the adult female. The egg may hatch into an individual which resembles the adult in all features except size, e.g., the cockroach, or into one which is very different, e.g., a beetle grub or moth caterpillar. In neither case, however, does the young insect have wings, these being found only in the adults. The larval stage is the one during which growth takes place; as the cuticle is firm, growth is limited by its elasticity. When this limit is reached the skin splits and is cast off, revealing a new skin underneath. This in turn is cast off until the larva has reached its maximum size. In the case of insects which hatch from the egg and resemble their parents, growth proceeds by a number of moults until the adult insect is formed, the wings becoming a little larger at each moult. The final moult produces a sexually mature adult. In the case of insects whose young are different, the final moult of the larval stage reveals a pupa, which is unlike both larva and adult. During this stage, which is relatively immobile and is generally spent within a silken or other type of cell or cocoon, considerable changes of internal organisation take place and from the pupal case the adult emerges, winged and sexually mature. After a day or so, mating takes place and the female commences to lay eggs. The life cycle of most of the important pests of stored products thus consists of four parts: egg, larva, pupa, adult. The larval stage is the one for growth; the adult stage is for reproduction and dispersal.

The duration of the life cycle varies considerably from

species to species. It may be as short as three weeks or as long as four years. In general it is shortened by increase of temperature and lengthened by decrease. For many species breeding is continuous and generation succeeds generation until the foodstuff is exhausted, provided conditions remain otherwise favourable. The effect of reduced temperature is to stop activity and growth and most stored products species pass the winter in this country in a state of hibernation at the stage of development reached at the end of the summer. This is usually as an adult or fully grown larva. In the case of other species, however, development may cease apparently independently of external conditions. For example, most of the fully grown larvæ of the cacao moth (*Ephestia elutella*) spin cocoons in August and do not change into pupæ until the following May; a few, however, continue their development normally, changing to pupæ from which adults emerge in September. Even under experimental conditions it is not possible to induce the 'resting' caterpillars to change to pupæ until several months have elapsed.

It is important to know as much about the various stages of development as possible in order that the most appropriate method of control may be applied at each stage. For example, one insecticide may be effective against all stages except the egg and an apparently successful treatment may have to be repeated later when the eggs have hatched and given rise to larvæ. As another example, the various methods used against the cacao moth (*Ephestia elutella*) are closely related to the habits of the insect at various stages. The caterpillars leave the food when they are fully fed and wander about the surface of the commodity for a short time. At this stage they can be killed by insecticide spraying or by trapping on sticky bands, methods which are not effective so long as the caterpillars are feeding inside the commodity. If control is not applied, many of the caterpillars migrate into cracks in the walls and ceiling of the warehouse where they spin cocoons and remain for many months in hibernation.

During this time they cannot be reached by sprays or dusts and it is difficult to reach them in sufficient concentration by fumigants used for the treatment of the warehouse rooms. The next vulnerable stage is the adult moth, which can be killed by insecticide films sprayed onto the surface of susceptible commodities or by insecticidal mists produced in warehouse rooms. Moths are killed by flying in the mists or by contact with the insecticidal film when they alight on the surface of the foodstuff to lay eggs. If these measures are not applied before the first moths emerge in the summer, the caterpillars which hatch from the eggs penetrate into the commodity where they are protected.

Most of the insect pests of stored products are beetles (Coleoptera), and moths (Lepidoptera). In the case of beetles, both larvæ and adults have mouth parts adapted for biting and therefore both can feed on stored products. The length of life of some adult beetles is prolonged, being sometimes over twelve months. In the case of moths, the adults have mouth parts adapted for sucking up fluids and cannot damage stored products. The larvæ have biting mouth parts and effect considerable damage.

Insect pests belonging to other orders are cockroaches (Orthoptera), book-lice (Psocoptera), silver fish (Thysanura), cheese skippers and blow flies (Diptera). Some insects prey upon the true pests; these are included in the groups of parasitic wasps (Hymenoptera) and bugs (Hemiptera).

Mites have a similar life history to insects. For example, the adult female flour mite (*Tyroglyphus farinae*) lays some 20–30 eggs. After four days the six-legged larva hatches and after feeding for a few days becomes inert and moults to produce an eight-legged nymph. This stage lasts 6–8 days and may be followed by a further active nymphal stage or by a relatively inert stage, 'the hypopus', which is adapted for dispersal and resistance to adverse conditions. Both stages are followed by a further nymphal stage, which moults in due course to produce the adult. Under normal conditions the whole life cycle takes from 17 to 28 days and, so long as conditions remain favourable, mites will continue to feed almost down to freezing point.

The environment of the stored products pest has some peculiar features and, to be successful, pests must adapt themselves to these conditions. The activities of man in growing and storing large masses of food for himself, provide incidentally a vast excess food supply for the pests. It is seldom that the stored products pest finds the supply of food a limiting factor. This may, however, occur where warehouses are left empty for years, but even there one will find that certain species can maintain themselves for long periods on dust and detritus spilt in the fabric of the building. These small populations can rapidly multiply when excess food is provided. The adult females generally lay large numbers of eggs, a high proportion of which reach maturity. For most species the life cycle is short, under favourable conditions, and it is therefore not long before the original population has multiplied manyfold. Under practical conditions, parasites have not been observed to exercise any great control, as they do not appear to be successful unless the host population is already large, by which time much of the infested commodity will have been damaged. Bacteria and viruses, however, are known to effect almost complete control of populations of certain caterpillars.

The food attacked by the pests is generally dry (in contrast to the condition of growing crops), as otherwise it would not remain free from attacks by bacteria and fungi, or, if a seed, would be liable to germinate. There would appear to be no lower limit, under experimental conditions, to the moisture content which insects can tolerate in food, since the mill moth (*Ephestia kühniella*) has been successfully reared on food almost devoid of water, and the khapra beetle (*Trogoderma granaria*), will live under very arid conditions in maltings. Generally speaking, however, little damage occurs if the moisture content of grain is below 8% and few mites will attack grain or flour which has a moisture content of less than 12%. For most of the insects and mites infesting commodities it is the relative humidity of the air in the spaces between the particles of the commodity which has the most influence. This relative humidity is mainly determined by the water content of the commodity itself and it is only in the surface layers exposed to the external atmosphere that diurnal changes occur. Many commodities, too, are poor conductors of heat, and the insects which attack the foodstuff are thus generally insulated from external changes by the buffering action of the material infested. Most pests can obtain sufficient water from that contained in the food, although it has been shown that where the water content is low, they can obtain water by the breakdown of carbohydrates in the food. On the other hand it is known that egg laying is greatly stimulated in some species if the adult female has access to liquid water. This is usually available in warehouses and similar places in fire buckets and also from the droppings of rodent pests. This is an interesting example of the inter-relation of mammal and insect food pests, also shown by the fact that certain insects will breed in rat droppings.

Certain commodities are susceptible only to attack by particular insects or mites. Thus sound whole grain is liable to damage only by a limited number of species which can penetrate the outer coat. Once the endosperm and germ have been exposed by these 'primary' pests, then a very large number of secondary pests are able to effect damage. The attacks of both primary and secondary pests may cause changes in the distribution of moisture in stocks of stored produce to such an extent that conditions may be made favourable for attack by moulds and bacteria, and, in extreme cases, even for sprouting of grain to take place. Many manufactured products, having already been altered by man, are liable to attack both by primary and secondary pests.

Many insects, found in stored products, do not feed directly upon the commodity but upon moulds or bacteria. Others feed upon the dead bodies of other pest species, on dead mammal and bird pests and on insect droppings and webbing. The presence of species of this group is an indication of a well established infestation, as is the presence of numbers of the group of parasitic and predatory insects (Plate 4).

Consideration of the part played by each species in attacking stored products is greatly assisted by research into the basic food requirements of insects and mites. Recent work has provided basic information regarding a number of stored products pests. It is thus possible to estimate the susceptibility of any particular product to attack by a particular species from a consideration of chemical composition and vitamin content.

The inter-relationships of the various species form an interesting subject of fundamental importance to the control of stored products pests. It is difficult, at the present state of knowledge, to forecast accurately what will be the likely development of any particular association of insects found in a stored product. A slight alteration of humidity or temperature may provide the slight change of conditions, which will favour the development of one species rather than another. Knowledge of the ecology of insects and mites will enable those responsible for the application of control measures to select the most appropriate method, including that of taking no action, if the particular conditions are such that the infestation may be expected to die out of its own accord.

4. How pests spread

The insect and mite pests fall broadly into two groups. There are those which can maintain themselves indefinitely in this country in unheated warehouses. There are others which, whilst they cause regular trouble during the summer, can only maintain themselves from year to year if they can find warm conditions during the winter.

The first group includes a number of insects and mites which have been known to be present in the British Isles for

a long period. Of indigenous pests in this group, one may
mention the meal worm (*Tenebrio molitor*), the grain moth
(*Tinaea granella*), the larder beetle (*Dermestes lardarius*), the
white-shouldered house moth (*Endrosis sarcitrella*), the
brown house moth (*Hofmannophila pseudospretella*), and
the grain weevil (*Calandra granaria*). There are others,
which although well established now, were only introduced
within relatively recent times. Of these one may mention
the mill moth (*Ephestia kühniella*), the golden spider beetle
(*Niptus hololeucus*) and the brown spider beetle (*Ptinus
tectus*). The mill moth was discovered in 1877 in a mill in
Saxony. It spread rapidly throughout the world, being
recorded from England in 1886, Canada in 1889, South
Africa in 1890, the U.S.A. in 1892. The brown spider beetle
(*Ptinus tectus*) is a native of Tasmania, and was not reported
in this country until 1892, in London. Between 1901 and
1904 it was again reported from London and Liverpool and
during subsequent years it spread rapidly over the country,
being reported from Ireland in 1916. In regard to the spread
of this species it is of interest to note that the adults do not
fly and that therefore almost the whole of its dispersal must
have been on the commodities which it infested. The golden
spider beetle (*Niptus hololeucus*) originated in the Near
East, where it was first reported in 1835; it reached England
in 1837 and during subsequent years was reported from
various parts of Europe. Now it is of interest to observe
that these species are not at all commonly found today in
commodities which are regularly imported into the United
Kingdom, nor is there any reason to suppose that they were
common in pre-war years. It only requires a very small
number of insects to be introduced to a favourable habitat
for them to multiply rapidly and soon spread to the limits
of their range. This is one of the reasons why special steps
have been taken to exterminate any individuals of the
hairy spider beetle (*Ptinus villiger*); this species is a serious
pest in Canada but has so far not established itself here.

Other established species are common inside the country

and are also regularly introduced from abroad. Here are included such serious pests as the cacao or tobacco moth (*Ephestia elutella*), the webbing clothes moth (*Tineola biselliella*), the cadelle beetle (*Tenebroides mauritanicus*), the grain weevil (*Calandra granaria*) and the Indian meal moth (*Plodia interpunctella*).

For the first group of species it might be possible to eradicate the pests concerned by a determined effort in our own warehouses and food factories, but as far as the latter are concerned it would also be necessary to establish a complete quarantine on imported goods and ensure that these were all treated before they entered the country.

The second group of pests includes a large number which are regularly imported into the United Kingdom on commodities, but which are unable to establish themselves under normal conditions of unheated storage. In this group are included such pests as the rust-red flour beetle (*Tribolium castaneum*), the coffee bean weevil (*Araecerus fasciculatus*), the tobacco beetle (*Lasioderma serricorne*), the lesser grain borer (*Rhizopertha dominica*), and the Angoumois grain moth (*Sitotroga cerealella*). The fig moth (*Ephestia cautella*), the copra beetle (*Necrobia rufipes*), and the rice weevil (*Calandra oryzae*) may be able to survive the winter and their life histories are being studied. Those insects so far mentioned are direct pests of food, but there are one or two household pests which can only maintain themselves in heated places, and which are not uncommonly found in goods brought into this country from abroad. These are the steam fly or cockroach (*Blatella germanica*) and Pharaoh's ant (*Monomorium pharaonis*). The latter, in particular, is a serious pest in hospitals, as it has the habit of forming colonies under concrete floors. The workers, in search of food, may crawl over helpless patients and even invade operating theatres carrying germs to sterilised materials. The insects of this main group normally die during the winter, owing to the effects of cold and damp, but very local warm conditions may enable them to survive.

Thus in one grain warehouse the rust-red flour beetle (*Tri-bolium castaneum*), could be found living throughout the year, keeping itself going in the winter in the vicinity of a hot exhaust pipe. Flour stored in closed-down cotton mills during the war was particularly susceptible to pest attack, because the buildings were kept warm throughout the winters to protect the idle machinery from rust. Insects may also carry over the winter in 'heating' grain, as has already been described. From the practical point of view these species are particularly dangerous during the summer months and commodities imported during the spring would normally have to be treated in such a way as to kill the pests. But commodities infested with these species imported during the autumn may, under certain circumstances be left safely in store without treatment during the winter, as the cold weather will act as a natural control. It is important, however, in this connection, that the decision should be based on expert advice, which will take into account the species of insects present and the conditions under which the commodity will be stored.

5.   *The prevention and control of infestation.*

The prevention and control of infestation should be treated as a continuous process, commencing at the farm (whether in this country or overseas) and continuing through to the consumer. It is generally more economical, efficient and wholesome to prevent insect outbreaks than to control them once they have occurred and caused damage. The whole process of insect prevention and control should be carried out with skilled guidance and advice so that all relevant considerations may be taken into account. Too many of the measures at present adopted in the world are palliative and used without proper appreciation of the fundamental biological, chemical and physical principles involved. It is of particular economic importance that measures for the prevention and control of infestation should entail the minimum interference with normal estab-

Plate. 1.—Hybrid and parent maize plants. For explanation see text, page 21. (From the Inheritance of Physiological Characters, by E. Ashby, Annals of Botany, volume XLIV, 1930, *by permission of the Oxford University Press*).

Plate 2.—Maize damaged by the rice weevil (*Calandra oryzae*).
Exit holes, dusty excreta and live and dead weevils can be seen.
Magnification x 2½. (*Crown Copyright reserved*).

*Plates 3, 5, and 11 from J. A. Freeman and E. E. Turtle, " The
Control of Insects in Flour Mills" by permission of the Controller
H.M. Stationery Office. Plates 2, 4, 6—10, 12—14 by permission
of the Director of Infestation Control, Ministry of Agriculture and
Fisheries.*

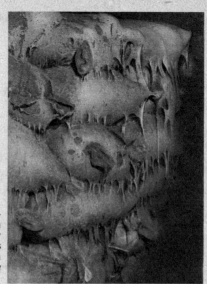

Plate 3. — Bagged oil-seeds covered with "wandering" caterpillars of the cacao moth (*Ephestia elutella*) (*Crown Copyright reserved*)

Plate 4.—Oilcake damaged by caterpillars of the rice moth (*Corcyra cephalonica*). Also to be seen are a dead adult and live larva of the scavenging beetle, *Dermestes ater*. Magnification x 1½. (*Crown Copyright reserved*).

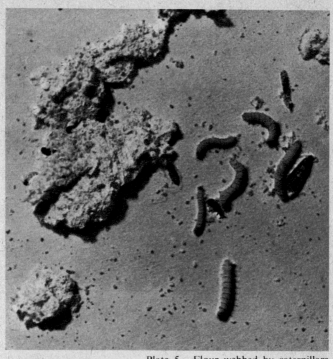

Plate 5.—Flour webbed by caterpillars of the mill moth, *Ephestia kühniella*. In addition to the caterpillars, there is a dead moth and two dead cadelle beetles (*Tenebroides mauritanicus*). Natural size. (*Crown Copyright reserved*).

Plate 6.—Cheroots damaged by caterpillars of the tropical tobacco moth, *Setomorpha rutella*. (*Crown Copyright reserved*).

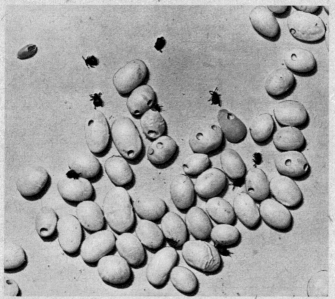

Plate 7.—Beans damaged by the bean beetle, *Acanthoscelides obtectus.*
Exit holes and adult beetles can be seen. (Slightly reduced). (*Crown
Copyright reserved*).

Plate 8.—Wheat damaged by heating as the result of severe insect
attack. The caked portions stand up instead of flowing freely. (*Crown
Copyright reserved.*)

Plate 9.—A sticky band trap for caterpillars on a pillar in a warehouse. A large number of caterpillars of the cacao moth (*Ephestia elutella*) have been trapped on the band but some can be seen above it, having crawled over the bodies of those stuck on the band. (*Crown Copyright reserved*).

Plate 10.—Tidy stacking of goods in small piles. Note the dunnage raising the goods off the concrete floor. (*Crown Copyright reserved*).

Plate 11.—Spraying insecticide on to bagged goods. (*Crown Copyright reserved*).

Plate 12.—An insecticide smoke cartridge shortly after ignition.
(*Crown Copyright reserved*).

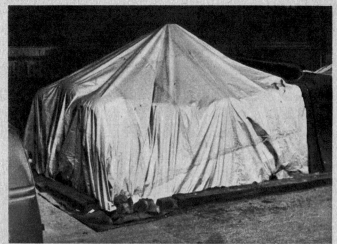

Plate 13.—A stack of bagged goods has been covered with this sheet of barrage balloon fabric so that fumigation can be carried out. (*Crown Copyright reserved*)

Plate 14.—Inspectors examining oilseeds in a barge. (*Crown Copyright reserved*).

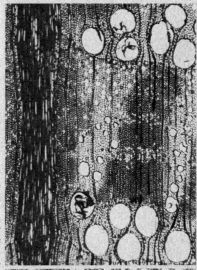

Plate 15.—Oak (*Quercus robur*). A ring-porous hardwood. Above the large springwood vessels (near the bottom) is a summerwood zone containing smaller vessels embedded in a light-coloured mass of tracheids, and on either side of this, darker fibrous tissue, crossed here and there by irregular bands of parenchyma. On the left is a large medullary ray (dark) and parallel to it several narrow rays. Some of the large vessels contain tyloses. (*Crown Copyright reserved*).

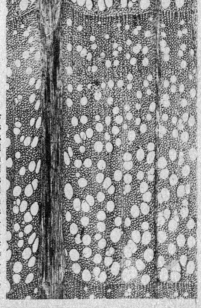

Plate 16.—Beech (*Fagus sylvatica*). A diffuse-porous hardwood. The vessels which decrease in size and number gradually from springwood to summerwood are embedded in fibrous tissue; a zone of flattened fibres marks the end of each annual ring. Parenchyma is limited to a few (light-coloured) isolated cells. As in oak, wide rays and more numerous narrow ones are present. (In many hardwoods the rays are fairly uniform in size). (*Crown Copyright reserved*).

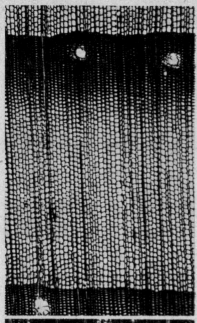

Plate 17.—Scots pine or Baltic redwood (*Pinus sylvestris*). A softwood. The structure is more regular than in hardwoods, being composed principally of tracheids in radial series, thin-walled in the spring-wood and thicker-walled and darker in the summer-wood. The rays are very narrow and inconspicuous. The two large holes are resin ducts. (*Crown Copyright reserved*).

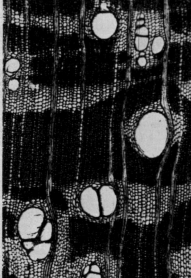

Plates 18—20.—Photomicrographs showing three tropical woods in cross-section. (X 35). Definite growth rings, so well marked in temperate woods, are absent.

Plate 18.—Iroko or "African teak" (*Chlorophora excelsa*). The masses of light-coloured parenchyma in which the vessels are embedded contrast with the dark fibrous tissue and form a distinctive pattern. (*Crown Copyright reserved*).

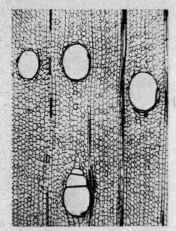

Plate 19.—Balsa (*Ochroma* spp.). The lightest of the commercial hardwoods (average density: 6 lb./cu. ft.). All the cells are exceedingly thin-walled and the cell cavities correspondingly large. (*Crown Copyright reserved*).

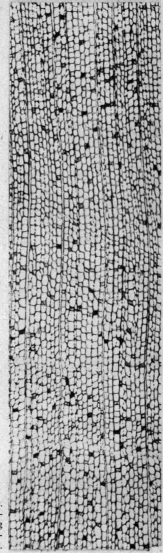

Plate 20.—*Podocarpus montana*. A tropical softwood. The dark-coloured cells are resin-containing parenchyma; resin ducts are absent. (*Crown Copyright reserved*).

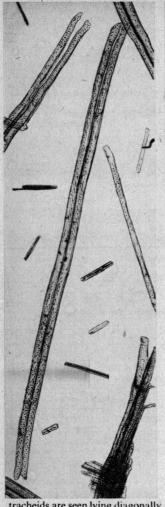

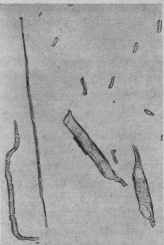

Plates 21 and 22.—The various kinds of wood cells. ($\times$ 50). By treatment with chemical reagents the cementing layer between the cells has been dissolved and the wood separated into its constituent units. (*Crown Copyright reserved*).

Plate 21 (above).—Oak (*Quercus robur*). A hardwood. On the extreme left is a well-pitted tracheid and a needle-shaped fibre. On the right are two segments of a small vessel showing the oval rims where they were joined. Above are several small ray and parenchyma cells.

Plate 22 (left).—Spruce (*Picea abies*). A softwood. Two complete tracheids are seen lying diagonally. These bear numerous bordered pits and near the middle are a group of smaller pits where the tracheids were connected to a ray. In the bottom right-hand corner part of a ray remains connected to a group of tracheids. The small scattered elements are ray cells, some of which have resinous contents.

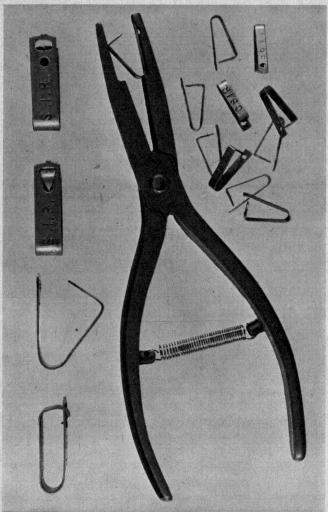

Plate 23.—Tagging apparatus showing metal V-shaped tags, some open and some closed, and the pliers which are used to fasten them to the gill cover of the fish. (*By permission of the Australian Commonwealth Council for Scientific and Industrial Research*).

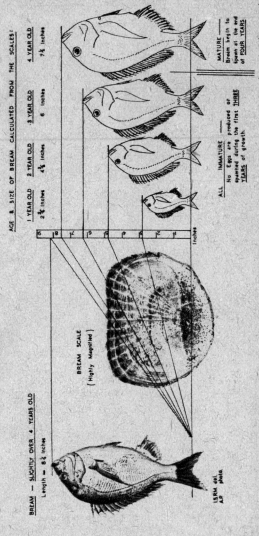

AGE & GROWTH — AUSTRALIAN BREAM (ACANTHOPAGRUS AUSTRALIS)

AGE & SIZE OF BREAM CALCULATED FROM THE SCALES:

| 1 YEAR OLD | 2 YEAR OLD | 3 YEAR OLD | 4 YEAR OLD |
| 2⅜ Inches | 4⅛ Inches | 6 Inches | 7½ Inches |

ALL IMMATURE ——
No Eggs are produced or spawned during the first THREE YEARS of growth.

MATURE ——
Bream begin to spawn at the end of FOUR YEARS.

BREAM SCALE (Highly Magnified)

BREAM — SLIGHTLY OVER 4 YEARS OLD
Length = 8½ Inches

I.S.R.M. del.
A.P. photo.

Plate 24.—Scale reading. This diagram shows how a scale taken from a fish may be used to calculate the size reached by the fish at previous stages of its life. (By permission of the Australian Commonwealth Council for Scientific and Industrial Research and I.S. R. Munro).

lished commercial methods of handling and fabricating commodities, unless, of course, these methods are an encouragement to the development of pests. The cost of the control should bear a reasonable relationship to the value of the material which has to be treated or protected and also to the likely consequential losses which would occur if the infestation were allowed to proceed unchecked.

(a) Prevention

The basis of prevention is good housekeeping or hygiene. The movement of stored products inevitably results in some of the commodity being spilt. Such spillage is also produced by the activity of rats and mice, which carry some of the food material into the fabric of buildings. Pests can easily breed in dust and spillage for long periods even when bulk commodities are not in store and the pests are ready waiting to attack the clean goods when they arrive. It is an essential of good warehouse-keeping that all spillage and dust should be removed as soon as possible after movement has finished and that these sweepings should be stored quite separately from the main bulk of the commodity. Where conditions permit they should be destroyed or fumigated. Cleanliness of warehouses can be best maintained not by sweeping alone, but by the use of powerful vacuum cleaners, which remove both dust and insects into a bag, the contents of which can be later destroyed.

Cleanliness in warehouse rooms filled with goods is greatly assisted if the goods are packed in sound containers (bags, boxes, drums) and by careful stacking of the goods in small piles so that they may be readily inspected and the floor spaces cleaned. Where the floor is likely to be damp it is essential that the goods should be raised from the ground, generally on wooden dunnage, so that they cannot get damp and consequently, be attacked more readily by mites, moulds and insects. A further advantage of small pile stacking is that if an insect outbreak occurs it can be localised to the pile concerned, which may be fumigated or removed. (Plate 10).

Many warehouses in this country are old, ill lit and diffi-cult to keep clean. It is essential that when new warehouses and food factories are designed, proper attention should be paid to the problems of maintenance of hygienic conditions as an aid to pest control.

It would, however, be a mistake to place heavily infested commodities untreated into sound storage. Where possible, therefore, infested goods should be segregated from sound goods. This does not mean, of course, that the infested goods may then be left to rot. The basic reason for the segregation is to reduce the extent of the problem by con-fining the infestation to the goods already infested and not merely to put the infestation out of mind. Local isolation of sound or infested commodities is often effected within ware-houses by the use of bands of sticky materials or by barriers of insecticidal dusts. Such measures are only of use against crawling pests. (Plate 9).

(b) Control

However careful one may be in the application of the basic hygienic preventive measures, the defences some-times break down and goods become infested. In addition one is faced with the problem of dealing with a constant inflow of infested imports. It is necessary to have available as large as possible a number of control measures, so that the one may be used which is best adapted to the particular problem.

Any control method must conform to certain criteria. The method should :

(1)   kill the insects or mites present under the conditions of treatment or at least produce a high percentage mortality.

(2)   do no harm to the commodity at time of treatment, leave no harmful residues nor alter the nature of the commodity.

and (3) be harmless to those who have to apply it or, if dangerous, be capable of use under strictly defined con-ditions.

The control methods available fall into three main classes. These are (*a*) mechanical, (*b*) physical and (*c*) chemical.

Mechanical methods

The use of the industrial vacuum cleaner as a means of removal of dust and insects has already been mentioned; a similar application of the same principle is found in flour mills and granaries which have built-in suction systems.

Materials which are infested by insects and mites living freely between the particles (but not boring within them as do weevil grubs) may be treated by sieving. For this method to be reasonably successful it is necessary that the pests should be appreciably different in size from the particles of the material from which they are to be removed. Alternatively insects and mites can be removed by blowing them out by a strong current of air. Such a treatment, for example, will remove a high proportion of mites from grain. However all screening and aspirating methods always leave a few individuals behind to act as centres of breeding.

A more recent development of mechanical methods has been the development of a machine which applies the principle of centrifugal force to the treatment of granular materials. Flour fed to the machine is thrown by centrifugal force between two flat steel discs which revolve on a central shaft at some 3,500 revolutions per minute. Small round hardened steel posts are closely spaced between the discs at their circumference. The impact of the flour against the revolving discs and posts and against the housing of the machine is so great, that all insect stages, including the egg, are killed. Its has been found by experiment that a very high proportion of the insects and mites infesting a treated commodity are killed by this process, which is very suitable for the continuous treatment of materials prior to packing.

Physical methods

These are mainly limited, under practical conditions, to the use of heat and cold. The biological principles under-

lying their use have already been described. In practice the
use of heat and cold offers considerable difficulties. For the
treatment of warehouse and factory rooms radiators can be
used at the height of the summer to increase the temperature to lethal levels. In countries which have cold winters
the windows may be opened and the building allowed to
cool down at the depths of winter. But for the treatment of
commodities the high temperatures necessary to effect control of insects are so close to those which are liable to cause
damage to the commodity itself that the practical use of
heat is difficult. Thus the quality of flour may be reduced
if wheat is heated very much above 140° F. and heating of
wheat for insect control alone is a costly and uneconomic
operation. However, if grain is to be heated for the purpose
of drying it to a safe moisture content level, it is practicable
to combine both drying and insect control. It has been
suggested from time to time that heat might be applied by
electrical methods, but in cases so far investigated the cost
has been out of proportion to the quantity of material
which could be treated. Heating is a useful domestic
method of control for small quantities of foodstuffs. The
use of cold for general use is more common. Thus many
people place furs into cold storage during the summer at
temperatures which inhibit the development of the common
clothes moth. Cold storage has also been used for the control of the tobacco moth (*Ephestia elutella*) and the tobacco
beetle (*Lasioderma serricorne*) in stored tobacco. Under
practical conditions, the reduction of temperature in a large
mass of material takes a long time and is expensive, for the
lowering of temperature must take place throughout the
mass of the material being treated. During the period of
cooling the insects may become 'cold-hardy' and resistant
to the low temperatures. The cost and duration of this
method generally confines its use to particularly valuable
commodities and to goods which cannot be dealt with by
any other method, e.g. for foods in tins which only have
small holes open to the air.

Chemical methods

The chemical methods fall mainly into the following groups: (*a*) sprays, (*b*) dusts and smokes, and (*c*) fumigants.

Insecticidal sprays used for the prevention and control of infestation by insect and mite pests of stored foods usually consist of an oil carrier in which the insecticidal principle is dissolved or suspended. The spray may be produced by a hand sprayer, but in large warehouses it is more common to employ paint spraying guns operated by compressed air (Plate 11). Sprays may be applied as mists to kill flying insects, but such mists are much less persistent than films. The usual technique is to spray in such a way as to produce a thin film of spray over the surface of the commodity to be protected, as well as on the floor, walls and ceiling of the warehouse room. Such films remain toxic to insects for long periods (the time largely depends on the nature of the surface sprayed) so that any insects which crawl on them die sooner or later. The most common insecticidal principle in use is extract of pyrethrum flowers; the recently developed synthetic insecticides (D.D.T. and benzene hexachloride) may also be used, but only under conditions where they do not come into contact with food. Whereas pyrethrum is known to be non-poisonous to human beings and domestic animals, there is so far insufficient information about the possible long-term effects of continued ingestion by human beings of the synthetic insecticides, and their admixture with foods is not recommended by toxicologists. The active principles used in sprays and active dusts all fall into the class of 'contact poisons', i.e. they kill by penetrating through the insect or mite cuticle and not by being ingested. All three insecticides mentioned injure insects by damaging the nervous system. Poisons which have to be eaten by insects, known as 'stomach poisons,' which are widely used for the control of pests of growing crops, are little used for killing storage pests. Most of these poisons are not only lethal to insects but also to man and domestic animals, and should be used only when there is no danger of the insecticide used coming into contact with foodstuffs or being eaten accidentally by man or animals.

Dusts fall generally into two classes. *Active dusts* rely for their action on poisoning the insects by contact in the same way as sprays. Many dusts of this type consist of a small quantity of insecticidal principle mixed with a large volume of inactive dust to act as a carrier. *Inert dusts*, on the other hand, act by physical interference with the metabolism of insects or mites. Wigglesworth has demonstrated that finely divided aluminium oxide dust acts by abrading the outer layer of wax of the insect cuticle. Once this layer has been removed, the rate of evaporation of water increases and the insect or mite dries up and dies. Other inert dusts may act by blocking up the spiracles and so suffocating the insect. An inert dust known as 'katelsousse' (a mixture of finely ground rock phosphate and sulphur) is used for the protection of grain in warm countries, particularly Egypt. In this country a finely ground calcium sulphate dust has been used for the control of mites.

In practice in this country it has been found that the mixing of dust with grain on a large scale is subject to serious commercial disadvantages. The operation of mixing the dust is difficult and the dust produced during commercial handling is obnoxious to workpeople. Dusts are generally used for the treatment of empty rooms, for the isolation of infested stacks of goods and under conditions where sprays are inadvisable.

A modification of the dust and spray is the smoke (Plate 12). It has been found possible to mix insecticidal principles with smoke-producing materials so that on ignition a dense smoke is produced which carries the principle to all parts of the space treated. This forms a useful method where spraying cannot reach the surfaces and where the condition of the structure is such that sealing for fumigation is impracticable.

Fumigation
Fumigation may be defined as the use of toxic gases for

the control of pests. The toxic gases used enter the insects through their respiratory systems and then kill them by interference with their enzyme systems. For example it is known that hydrogen cyanide specifically destroys the respiratory enzymes. Fumigation is a method which is capable of dealing with established infestations within bulks or stacks of commodities in contrast to spraying, which only affects those insects which actually come into contact with the spray. Fumigation is also carried out in empty warehouse rooms, flour mills, the holds of ships, etc, for the control of insects in the structure. Ideal fumigants vaporise readily at ordinary temperatures, are highly toxic at low concentrations, penetrate commodities rapidly and, conversely, disperse rapidly after the fumigation has been completed. Such fumigants should, as far as possible, be non-inflammable and non-poisonous to man and domestic animals. The most common fumigants in use in this country are hydrogen cyanide; ethylene oxide carbon-dioxide mixtures; methyl bromide; and, for small-scale applications, a mixture of carbon tetrachloride and ethylene dichloride. The principal disadvantage of fumigation is the necessity of ensuring the air-tightness of the space to be treated, and the dangerous nature of the chemicals used. In practice the application of fumigants is done by commercial 'servicing' firms, who employ highly skilled workmen. The operations are carried out under the general provisions of Home Office regulations, designed to ensure the safety of the public and the workmen (Plate 13).

6. *General conclusions*

Industrial entomology has been one of the most neglected fields of applied biology. Whereas for many years there has been no lack of research and application into problems of agricultural and medical entomology, those of industrial entomology have received only scant attention in this country; in the United States of America the subject has received equal attention with those of agricultural ento-

mology and public health. After the work of the Royal
Society Grain Pests (War) Committee during the 1914-8
war, no official or University research department paid any
attention to this subject until the late twenties, when a
series of researches in this field were started in the Department of Entomology of Imperial College, London
University. During the period immediately preceding the
recent war, pressure by industry led to the carrying out of a
survey of the insect infestation of grain, as the result of
which the Government Department of Scientific and Industrial Research established the Pest Infestation Research
Laboratory at Slough, as a permanent part of its organisation. As the war progressed the Ministry of Food found it
necessary to establish its own organisation for the practical
application of control in food stores, ships and transport.
Barnett, in his article 'The War against Rodents' in NEW
BIOLOGY 2, has told of the work of this organisation in the
control of rats and mice. On the entomological side similar
work has been done. Inspection at all stages of import,
manufacture and distribution (Plate 14) as a basis for control action has ensured a logical application of sound
scientific principles of prevention and control.

In the international field a conference of European
countries was held in London in November 1945 to study
this problem and resulted in the establishment of a small
committee as part of the organisation of the Emergency
Economic Committee for Europe. The work of this organisation led to the establishment of a new control organisation
in Belgium and to the improvement of the laws relating to
this subject in other European countries as well as to the
exchange of much valuable technical information. The
United Nations Food and Agricultural Organisation, as
already stated, has taken a keen interest in infestation
control, as a means of solving the problem of world food
shortages, and called a meeting of experts from all over the
world in London in August, 1947. So many of the pests are
carried in commodities in world trade and so many of the

losses occur in countries which are backward in their development that it is only by the greatest amount of co-operation between countries that the losses can be prevented.

This necessarily condensed account of the field of infestation control will, it is hoped, have shown the large number of interesting problems which still remain to be solved both on the purely biological side and on the development of new and improved methods of control. Under present conditions it is important that no waste of food that can be prevented should be allowed to take place, and the losses from insects and mites represent a large potential saving.

ACKNOWLEDGEMENTS AND FURTHER READING

The author and editors are indebted to the Ministry of Agriculture and Fisheries for permission to make use of unpublished material and photographs. The biology of many of the insects mentioned and a full account of many methods of prevention and control are given in *Insect Pests of Food; The Control of Insects in Flour Mills* by J. A. Freeman and E. E. Turtle (H.M.S.O. 1947). A popular exposition of the subject is given in *Insects and Industry* by J. W. Munro (Ernest Benn Ltd., 1929). A detailed account of the conditions in granaries and similar structures in this country just before the war is given in *Report on a survey of infestation of grain by insects*, by J. W. Munro (H.M.S.O. 1940, reprinted 1947). For general entomology the most useful books are *Outlines of Entomology* by A. D. Imms (Methuen 1942) and *Recent Advances in Entomology* by the same author (Churchill, 1937).

The Biology and Properties of Wood

BY E. W. J. PHILLIPS

Photogravure illustrations betweeen pp. 64 and 65.

EVEN in these days of timber famine when greater efforts are being made to economise in its use than to further its sale, wood still plays an intimate part in the everyday life of each one of us – 'from the cradle to the grave.' Perhaps the search for substitutes to overcome the present-day scarcity of timber relative to the expanding demands of industry has led to a keener and wider appreciation of the unique combination of properties to be found in wood. There is greater need than ever to take full advantage of its special properties and take into account its limitations; to guard against such waste as using it in the unduly large sizes often used in the past and to take precautions to guard against its deterioration.

The properties of wood are closely bound up with the life history of the tree, and in the following article an attempt is made to give the would-be user some picture of what goes on inside the tree-trunk – how the wood structure is formed and how its mode of growth and the details of its construction affect the quality of the product and its utilization.

A convenient point at which to start consideration of wood production is at the seedling stage of the tree, say, towards the end of the first year's growth. The cellular organisation which is to produce the timber tree has then been built up into miniature tree form by the enlargement and sub-division of the cells present in the seed; at this stage external differentiation into roots, stem, leaves, lateral

74

and terminal buds has taken place. The following year the terminal bud will develop and continue the height growth of the young tree while the lateral buds produce the branches. Dissection of the young stem under the microscope shows it to consist of a thin outer sheath of protective *bark* consisting of small box-like cells; then a layer of *phloem* (*bast* or *inner bark*) consisting of vertically elongated cells concerned with the transport of the foodstuffs photosynthesized by the leaves; next comes the core of harder

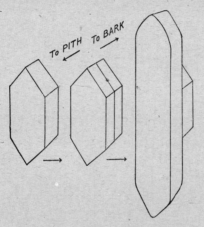

Fig. 1—The formation of a wood cell by the cambium (diagrammatic). The fully developed cambial cell (left) undergoes division into two by the formation of a tangential wall (centre). The inner cell (i.e., towards pith) resulting from the division is shown (right) commencing to elongate, later to become a fibre; the outer cell (i.e., towards bark) remains to undergo subdivision and so to initiate further wood cells.

material – the *wood* itself – consisting principally of elongated cells; and finally the *pith*, a slender axial rod composed of soft, more or less globular cells.

Close examination shows that between the phloem and

the wood lies a single layer of thin-walled, boat-shaped cells, flattened in the circumferential or tangential plane; this is the all-important *cambium* which is responsible for

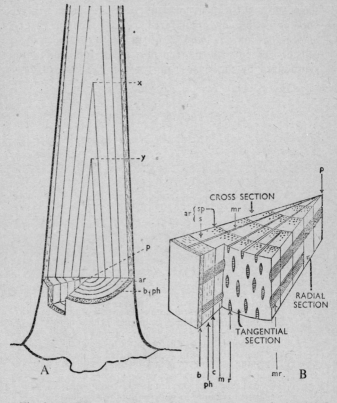

Fig. 2—A. Diagrammatic view of a young tree trunk showing 5 annual growth cones in longitudinal section and cross-section. y, tip of first year's woody growth; ar, annual ring; b, bark; p, pith; ph, phloem; x, tip of second year's woody growth. B. Wedge-shaped block taken from position shown in Fig. 2 A. It shows, diagrammatically, the general lay-out of the principal structural components. ar, annual ring; b, bark; c, cambium; mr, medullary ray; p, pith; ph, phloem; s, summerwood; sp, springwood.

the progressive thickening of the stem. The process by which this is brought about is as follows: each cambial cell divides into two by the formation of a wall in the vertical tangential plane; of the two cells so formed the inner one grows in size and develops into a wood cell while the outer one remains as part of the cambium, later to undergo further division (Fig. 1). In the course of the growing season each cell of the cambial sheath gives rise to a radial row of wood cells in this way. From time to time the cambial cells increase in number by dividing sideways (i.e. by a vertical wall in the radial plane) to keep pace with the growth expansion of the woody core. Occasionally the cambium forms new phloem cells and in this case the *inner* cell resulting from the tangential division into two remains as part of the cambium and the *outer* cell develops into the phloem element.

Growth of the tree restarts in the spring with the unfolding of the buds and simultaneously the cambium resumes its formation of wood. As the wood elements (*springwood*) formed at this season are larger and, in some species, differ in arrangement from those formed towards the end of the previous year's growth (*summerwood*) the junction of the two contrasting zones stands out as a visually distinct ring on the cleanly cut cross-section of the stem. Each year the new wood is formed as a continuous conical sheath over the previous year's wood, the upper portion of the cone being formed by the shoot developing from the terminal bud (Fig. 2). The number of annual rings to be seen on any given cross-section will obviously depend on the height in the tree at which it is taken, so that when using these rings to estimate the age of the tree it is necessary to examine a section taken at or near ground level. In the tropics where tree growth is not periodically suspended for any considerable time each year, distinct growth rings are normally lacking.

As the branches originating from the lateral buds develop, together with their cambial layer continuous with that of the main stem, each new wood sheath extends over these branches as well so that the conical sheath of the stem becomes rather like a multi-armed overcoat, or more accurately, since it lies under the bark and phloem, like a multi-armed vest. The basal portions of these branches become gradually embedded in the stem as the latter grows in thickness and constitute the knots found when the tree is sawn into timber.

A separate cambium (*cork cambium*) is formed just under the bark and this produces new bark cells as the older bark on the outside becomes split or thrown off by the expansion of the wood underneath. In some species the cork cambium forms a considerable amount of persistent bark; the cork of commerce is produced in this way, principally by the cork oak (*Quercus suber*).

Before considering in detail the various kinds of cells which make up the wood structure, it is pertinent to note the functions which the stem performs as part of the standing tree. Firstly, it provides mechanical support for the branches and leaves of the crown which must be kept up to receive the light necessary for photosynthesis despite competition from the crowns of neighbouring trees. Secondly, the stem provides channels for the translocation and storage of the photosynthesized carbohydrates upon which the whole life of the tree depends. Thirdly, the stem provides the channel for carrying up to the leaves the dilute solution of mineral salts, commonly referred to as *sap*, from the roots which absorb it from the soil. These three functional requirements are met by specialized kinds of cellular tissue (Fig. 3).

The *mechanical strength* of the stem is provided mainly by the *fibres* which are hollow needle-shaped cells usually around 2 mm. in length arranged with their long axes more or less parallel to that of the trunk. The fibre wall is often thick in comparison with the central cavity, and in the thick-walled fibres of some dense woods hardly any cavity can be discerned, while in light, weak woods the fibre wall is thin and the cavity correspondingly large (see Plates 15-20). In cross-section under the microscope they appear as small closely packed cells forming the general groundwork of the structural pattern.

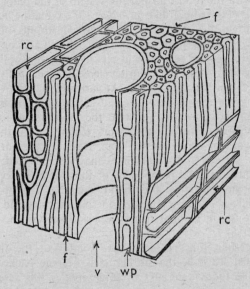

Fig. 3—Highly magnified view of cube of wood (of approximately 1/100 mm. side) showing the form and arrangement of the wood cells. f, fibre; rc, ray cell; v, vessel; wp, wood parenchyma cells.

The young fibre cell grows in length, sliding its pointed ends amongst the adjacent cells, until it is several times as long as its parent cambial cell; its wall then thickens, the living protoplasm and cell contents disappear and the fibre takes no further active part in the life of the tree. A few thin places (or *pits*) may be present here and there in the wall connecting the fibre cavity to those of adjacent cells; these pits may play some part in the early life of the fibre after elongation of the young cell but more probably they are merely vestigial structures which have lost their function during the evolution of the species – a parallel case to the appendix in Man.

The *food transport and storage system* of the wood connects with the food transporting system of the phloem and consists of the ribbon-like *medullary rays*, radiating horizontally about the stem axis, and vertical strands of *wood parenchyma* cells. Both rays and parenchyma are composed of small box-like cells having pits in their thin walls connecting them with neighbouring elements, principally those of the sap-conducting system. At various levels the vertical parenchyma crosses the rays and at these junctions there are also pit connections so that the food system forms a kind of three-dimensional network reminiscent of the steel framework of a modern building. Rays are present in all woody species and accordingly may be regarded as an essential functional component of the wood. The vertical parenchyma, on the other hand, does not appear to be essential; it is entirely lacking in some species and varies enormously in amount from species to species (cf. Plates 16 and 18).

At certain times of the year, notably at the time of autumnal leaf-fall, the storage cells become packed with insoluble food materials; in some species this reserve is chiefly in the form of starch grains (e.g. ash, oak) and in others as fat globules (*e.g.* many conifers, birch, lime). With the onset of growth in the spring some depletion takes place to meet the needs of the developing leaves and to furnish the raw materials for new tissue throughout the tree including the new sap-conducting elements of the springwood. During the summer the photosynthetic activity of the leaves permits of the reserves being restored in readiness for the following growing season, but this may not be possible if a heavy crop of seed is borne, and in many tree species it may be some years before the food reserve is completely restored to a level which permits another full production of fruit and seed. In sweet chestnut, elm and garden fruit trees a full seed year occurs every 2-3 years, in pine and oak every 3-5 years, and in beech the interval varies from 10 to 15 years.

The storage and re-distribution of food materials ranks high amongst the many physiological miracles of plant life. In its mobile form the food consists mainly of soluble sugars, which, after their formation in the leaves, pass downwards *via* the phloem and thence *via* the rays into the inner part of the storage system in the wood. This translocation in the wood is accomplished by diffusion from cell to cell and the necessary sugar concentration gradients to ensure such movement are maintained by the coordinated activity of catalytic systems in the protoplasm of each cell in the series, the soluble sugars being converted into insoluble starch or fat when it is necessary to reduce the sugar concentration. When demand is made on the storage cells, presumably by means of some hormone mechanism, the cell catalysts mobilize the reserves by converting them back to a soluble form and reverse diffusion gradients are established so that the sugars reach the growing points of the buds and anywhere else they are required. In very cold winters the food reserves may serve to protect the storage cells against frost damage: a temporary transformation of the insoluble reserves to sugar takes place, thus increasing the concentration of the watery solution which fills the cells and lowering the freezing point. The protective effect is the same as that produced by the careful motorist when he dissolves glycerine in the radiator water of his car.

The *sap-conducting system*, the third important system to be considered, is confined exclusively to the wood; the phloem takes no part in this. In woods such as beech and oak the conducting elements, the *vessels*, form a conspicuous feature of the cross-section (Fig. 3 and Plates 18-22), appearing as open pores, many times larger than the surrounding fibres, and visible even to the naked eye. Unlike the elements already considered which are closed, tubular (fibres) or box-like (rays and parenchyma) cells, the vessels are continuous tubular structures running vertically, uninterrupted by cross walls, for considerable distances. They are of composite construction, each vessel starting off as a vertical strand of cells derived from the cambium. Each cell of the strand swells considerably and the top and bottom walls then dissolve to leave a continuous segmented tube, like a series of drain pipes (Plate 21).

Among the woods which possess vessels two different types of arrangement of the elements, as seen in cross-section, are recognisable, viz, the *ring-porous* type (e.g. oak, Plate 15) in which the vessels of the springwood portion of each growth zone are distinctly larger and more numerous than those of the later-formed part of the growth zone, and the *diffuse-porous* type (e.g. beech, Plate 16) in which no such ring-like aggregation of larger vessels occurs, but instead the vessels are more or less evenly scattered through-out the year's growth and the transition in size, if any, between the springwood and summerwood vessels is gradual.

So far reference has been made only to those woods possessing sap-conducting vessels. All these species belong to the great botanical class of flowering plants known as Angiosperms, the members of which are characterised by having their seeds enclosed in containers of some kind or another. All woods furnished by this class of plant are known as *hardwoods*. The other great class of timber-yielding plants are the Gymnosperms, which have naked seeds, and in particular the group Coniferae; these furnish timbers of a fundamentally different structure which are referred to technically as *softwoods*. Included amongst these are such well-known timbers as pine, spruce, Douglas fir and yew. Softwood species in general have needle-like leaves whereas hardwood species are usually broad-leaved. Again, the softwoods occur as extensive forests in the cool temperate regions of the world and, with few exceptions, only at high altitude elsewhere; on the other hand, the broad-leaved species are most abundant in the tropics where they are present in great variety and often attain large dimensions. Although there are only a hundred or so species yielding softwood timber compared with several thousand kinds of hardwoods, they provide the bulk of the wood consumed by the principal timber-using countries; in the United Kingdom softwoods normally furnish about nine-tenths of the total requirements.

The simple structure of softwoods enables them to be readily distinguished from hardwoods (Plate 17); vessels are absent and about 95 per cent of the wood is composed of fibre-like elements known as *tracheids* (Plate 22) which serve to carry out both the mechanical and sap-conducting functions performed respectively by the fibres and vessels of hardwoods. Tracheids are about 5 mm. long and are connected by numerous pits of complex structure (*bordered pits*) on their radial walls through which the sap passes from one tracheid to the next. Tracheids are not confined to softwoods; cells of similar character but much shorter in length are found in certain hardwoods, e.g. oak (Plate 15) and sweet chestnut.

The remainder of the softwood structure is composed of narrow rays, usually only one cell wide, and in some cases a small amount of vertical parenchyma and *resin ducts*. (Plate 17). These are relatively short vertical tubes into which resin is secreted from parenchymatous cells forming the tube wall; they play no part in sap conduction. Except in some tropical softwoods, the growth rings are clearly marked owing to the contrast in visual density between the thin-walled springwood tracheids and the thick-walled ones of the summerwood.

The terms *softwood* and *hardwood* date back to the days when but few timbers were in general use; the common hard timbers were those of the broad-leaved species, beech, oak and a few others, which came to be known as hardwoods in contradistinction to the relatively soft timbers of the needle-leaved pine and spruce. With the gradual introduction of a

wider range of timbers the conventional trade terms for the
two classes were adhered to, although this resulted in such
hard timbers as pitch pine being referred to technically as
'softwoods' and balsa and other quite soft kinds as
'hardwoods.'

The protoplasmic part of most of the cells found in wood
is short-lived, only the cell-walls persisting. Amongst these
are included the fibres, tracheids and vessels; the vessel segments may lose their protoplasm in a matter of days. In
contrast, the storage cells may continue to carry out transformation of food materials for several years, the period
depending on the species and the growth conditions. In sweet
chestnut the storage cells usually die after two years; in
beech and some pines they may remain alive for several
decades. When conditions favouring vigorous growth of the
tree prevail, the storage cells have a longer life. The outer
zone of the tree which contains living storage cells is known
as *sapwood* and the inner, central core, consisting entirely
of dead cells, as *heartwood*. The latter is often, but not in-
variably, the darker in colour, and in commercial practice,
only wood which is visually distinct from the sapwood is
counted as heartwood.

The course of events leading up to the death of the cells
and the formation of heartwood is probably as follows.
First, the conduction of sap by the vessels of the inner sapwood becomes slower and slower since the leaves' demand
for sap is largely met from that supplied by the newer wood.
With the cessation of sap conduction the means of removing
waste products from the living cells is lost and the carbon
dioxide generated by the respiration of these cells may then
reach toxic concentrations; a concentration of as much as
25 per cent of the total gas present has been found. Prior to
the death of the cells certain changes occur which may alter
the character of the wood considerably as it becomes transformed to heartwood; the nature and extent of these
changes varies from species to species. In oak, for instance,
the changes are substantial. The starch grains in the dying

cells are observed to coalesce, and when tested with iodine, no *longer yield the characteristic blue starch iodide but react strongly with tannin reagents. Ray and parenchyma cells adjoining the vessels may resume a form of growth, pushing out membranous balloon-like growths (*tyloses*) into the vessel cavities through the connecting pits. By this time the sap columns have become broken and the vessels partially filled with air, and with the production of tyloses resumption of sap conduction is definitely precluded. In other species plugs of gum, derived from the starch reserves, are extruded into the vessel cavities in place of or in addition to tyloses. Finally colouring matter is produced which may infiltrate throughout the cell walls of all the elements and this, together with the coloured residual contents of the dying cells, gives the wood a distinctive colour, often in marked contrast to the pale sapwood. In oak and many other common species, the colour difference is not striking, but in some woods such as rosewood the sapwood is near-white and the heartwood almost black. Sycamore, ash and spruce are examples of woods in which the cells die unobtrusively and form no distinctively coloured central core; strictly speaking such species have no technical heartwood, although the central core consists solely of dead cells, and tyloses may be present.

Heartwood formation, or at least death of the storage cells, goes on progressively after the tree has attained a certain age and may continue throughout the further life of the tree which, under favourable circumstances, may go on for hundreds or even thousands of years. Of the species commonly met with in this country, life spans of 3,000 years have been recorded for yew, 1,500 years for oak, 1,000 years for lime and 930 years for beech, while some of the Californian Big Trees (*Sequoia gigantea*) are believed to be over 4,000 years old. Even so, these huge old trees are substantially exceeded in height by some of the Australian Eucalypts which reach over 500 feet. Long before most trees approach such phenomenal ages or dimensions they die, possibly having outgrown the available resources of their environment, or become so infirm from internal fungal decay that the next gale terminates their career. Foresters have long recognised that it is not an economic proposition to allow trees to achieve their natural life-span, since beyond a certain age the formation of wood becomes very slow and the tree becomes more liable to attack by fungi. Thus oak is considered mature for felling at 150-200 years, beech at about 120 years, ash as early as 60 years and Scots pine at 50-80 years. Wood from near the centre of overmature trees is frequently found to contain horizontal fractures which, although not always previously visible, may result in sudden failure of the timber at a relatively low load when stressed. A probable cause of these cross-fractures has recently been put forward by M. R. Jacobs as a result of his investigation of the growth stresses and strains present in the standing tree. He showed that the newly formed wood is in a state of tension – like a stretched skin, and accordingly exerts a corresponding compression on the older inner wood. As successive layers of new wood are laid down over the old, so the compression on the inner layers progressively increases until actual failure of the wood occurs. This 'fibre tension' hypothesis also explains the binding on the saw which occurs in cross-cutting a log and the tendency of some timbers to split during cutting-up as soon as the restraint of adjacent wood is removed.

The properties of timber

The more significant facts concerning the production of wood by the growing tree have now been indicated and it remains to consider the properties of this raw material and its behaviour in use.

Wood has been seen to consist of a mass of cells of various shapes and sizes, and their cavities. The wood substance composing the cell walls is a stiff, hydrophilic gel having a specific gravity, when dry, of 1.5. X-ray examination in conjunction with microscopic studies of the cell wall after treatment with reagents has led to the conclusion that it consists essentially of a sponge-like skeletal structure composed of intermeshed chains of cellulose molecules, their general direction being in a steep vertical spiral. Interspersed in the meshes of the cellulose, which constitutes approximately 50 per cent of the weight of the dry wood, are a number of other substances which apparently serve to stiffen the framework, principally hemicelluloses, closely related to cellulose, and the more complex carbohydrate lignin; these last two constituents are present in almost equal parts. Slight variations in the proportions of these major constituents occur even within a single species, and there are also important differences in the small amount of mineral matter present. Timbers also vary considerably in the amount of wood substance present, in the size of the cells, the proportions of the different tissues present and in the relative arrangement of their elements. All these variations have a marked influence on the properties and utilization of the timber, as will be seen from the following notes.

In the conversion of the log one has to consider which of the numerous possible ways of cutting it up will yield the best return; the structure of the wood will influence the decision. Thus, in cutting species having large rays, e.g. oak and the Australian silky oak, the most valuable timber is obtained by sawing the wood radially, i.e. as nearly as possible parallel to the rays so that each board shows the handsome 'silver grain' figure produced by the flakes of light-coloured ray tissue so exposed which show up against the darker background of fibrous tissues. Mahogany is also best converted in this way, in this case to show the 'ribbon grain' figure due to the inclination of the fibres to the vertical axis differing in successive growth rings; this results in differential light reflection from the boards comparable to that shown by a freshly rolled lawn. This radial cutting or 'quarter-sawing' is a more costly process than 'plain-sawing' the log by successive parallel cuts, and with species having

prominent growth ring boundaries or other contrasting
structural features, plain-sawing may yield the more attrac-
tive boards, the contrasting tissues appearing in section as a
series of irregular but ornamental veins. For many con-
structional purposes, of course, timber is used in positions
where special decorative features are of no importance, and
in such cases the sawing is carried out with the sole object
of maximum yield. Conversion from the log is of necessity
a wasteful process and, on the average, the sawn timber
amounts to no more than 40 per cent of the volume of the
trimmed log; the rest is lost, mainly as bark and sawdust, in
squaring up, and in removing defects. In converting the
particularly valuable woods used for decorative veneers,
very thin saws are used, or alternatively the wood is sliced
with special knives to minimise the conversion losses.

Seasoning.   In a freshly felled log the cells contain a considerable quantity of water, amounting in some cases to
twice the weight of the wood substance present; this water
saturates the cell walls and partially or completely fills the
cell cavities. For reasons which will appear later it is necessary in the majority of cases to remove most of this water
before use. The drying process is known as 'seasoning' and
is usually carried out by piling the sawn boards in the open
air or in heated drying kilns. Air seasoning in the open is a
lengthy process; the old rule for oak boards is a year for
each inch in thickness. Early attempts to accelerate drying
by enclosing the timber in heated chambers caused heavy
degrade by splitting and distortion, and for a long time kiln
seasoning remained under a cloud. In these early days the
mistake was made of starting the actual drying at the com-
mencement of the kiln run. This resulted in rapid drying of
the outer layers of each board, but the shrinkage, which
normally occurs when wood dries, was prevented by the
inner, and still wet, core; in consequence splitting occurred
or, in less severe cases, the outer wood acquired a permanent set in the stressed condition. Subsequently, the inner
wood dried out, but was restrained from shrinking by the

hardened outer layer so that finally the seasoned board had its inner portion set in a stretched condition, with the outer layer, originally also set in a stretched condition, now subjected to a pull from the inner wood. Such timber is said to be 'casehardened' and this condition, unlike casehardening of metals, has nothing to recommend it; when the case-hardened board is planed or sawn, the balance of stresses is upset and distortion usually occurs.

Another seasoning defect known as 'collapse' is apt to appear in large-pored hardwoods and in softwoods having thin-walled tracheids if premature drying is permitted; the fragile elements actually cave in, presumably as the result of surface tension forces set up as water is withdrawn from the cell cavities.

Nowadays, it is realised that the wood must be warmed throughout its thickness before drying is allowed to start. This is achieved by warming the timber while a high humidity is maintained. The actual drying is then carried out by gradually raising the temperature and lowering the humidity at such a rate that a steadily decreasing moisture gradient is maintained, from the middle of the wood to the outside. In practice, the process is controlled by means of periodical moisture content tests on sample boards. The seasoned timber is examined for the presence of collapse or of any residual stresses, and if these are present the kiln load is given a stress-relieving or *reconditioning* treatment, analogous to the annealing of metals; this consists of steaming the timber for a few hours so that it becomes temporarily plastic and adjusts itself. Only slight superficial re-wetting occurs, and this usually dries off as the timber cools down.

The saving in drying time by kiln seasoning may be gauged from the fact that it is possible to season 1-inch boards more thoroughly in a month in this way than by a year in the open air. Properly handled, kiln drying can be of great assistance in these days of conveyor belts and mass production in keeping up a steady flow of ready-to-use timber without maintaining the vast stocks of slowly seasoning timber which would be necessary if reliance had to be placed on the uncertain method of air-seasoning.

A recent approach to the problem of maintaining a steady moisture gradient during air- or kiln-seasoning has been to use water-soluble chemicals, e.g. urea, in the form of paste or spray, applied to the surface of the wet timber. The substance dissolves in the sap of the outer cells and when drying from the surface commences this hygroscopic solution simultaneously attracts moisture from the interior and a steady diffusion from within outwards takes place. The process has the advantages of preventing premature drying of the exterior even when rapid drying conditions are employed and of facilitating the otherwise extremely difficult drying of thick timber.

With the advent of radio-frequency heating with its special property of rapidly heating up the interior of materials, a substantial acceleration of the seasoning process has been brought within the realms of possibility and has, in fact, been achieved on an experimental scale, reducing the seasoning period to a matter of hours or even minutes. It remains to be seen whether it is practicable to achieve satisfactory results with this method on a commercial scale and at a reasonable cost.

Shrinkage. As wood dries, the free water is gradually lost until the cell cavities are empty, leaving only the water saturating the cell walls. This stage of drying is known as the *fibre saturation point* (F.S.P.) and corresponds to a moisture content of about 30 per cent of the dry weight of the wood. Beyond this point removal of water occurs from between the meshes of the cellulose framework of the cell wall which have held water since their formation, possibly centuries before, and it is during the further drying period that splits and distortion are liable to be produced owing to the shrinkage which now begins and continues steadily right down to zero moisture content. The loss in volume varies from about 5 per cent in very light timbers to about 20 per cent in very heavy timbers. Since wood is normally dried for use to a moisture content approximately half-way between F.S.P. and the completely dry condition, the shrinkage, in practice, is about one-half of the above figures. As with other properties of wood, shrinkage varies according to the direction of the grain, a fact attributed to the orientation of the cellulose chains in the cell walls. Loss of water from between the long, almost vertical strands of cellulose causes substantial shrinkage in the horizontal plane, but has little effect on the vertical dimension. The transverse contraction is not uniform but is usually from one and a half to three times as great in the tangential as in the radial direction; a restraint imposed by the rays appears to be responsible for this differential shrinkage. Of the vertical elements, the fibres, which contain the bulk of the wood substance, play an important part, shrinking without deformation themselves but causing some tangential compression and radial extension of the weaker vessels and parenchyma. This effect of the anatomical structure accounts in part at least for the differences in shrinkage behaviour shown by different timbers. For an article which must keep its shape even under conditions of use which may cause changes in its moisture content, it is more important to select a timber which shrinks similarly in the radial and tangential directions of the grain rather than one which happens to have a low overall but marked differential shrinkage. Mahogany, a traditional species for precision woodwork, is an example of the former type of timber.

Wood being a hygroscopic material adjusts itself to the moisture condition of its surroundings by losing or absorbing moisture until an *equilibrium moisture content* is attained. In service it may encounter a wide range of humidities and, unless given a waterproofing treatment, will undergo moisture content and corresponding dimensional changes. Wherever the conditions of use are known beforehand the degree of seasoning should be matched with the average humidity conditions likely to be met with. Thus, for general carpentry in this country, a moisture content of about 20 per cent is suitable, and this can be attained by air-drying out-of-doors, while for furniture and woodwork to be used in normally heated rooms 12 per cent is advisable, and some form of heat seasoning is necessary.

Strength properties. In the various uses of timber, several strength properties come into play, singly or in combination. Thus, for example, a beam must offer not only resistance to bending, a property itself dependent on strength in compression, tension and shear, but must possess stiffness to avoid undue sagging, and hardness to prevent excessive crushing where it bears on the end supports.

Within a species each form of strength varies considerably, depending on grain direction, degree of seasoning and factors bound up with conditions of growth, including anatomical features and the presence of knots and other defects.

Strength is substantially higher along the grain in bending and compression strength, but lower in shear, and end-grain surfaces are harder than side-grain. A beam in which the grain has a 1 in 5 slope may be 50 per cent weaker than a straight-grained, but otherwise similar, beam. The weakening effect of knots is due primarily to the associated grain distortion rather than to any inherent weakness of the knot tissues. Some properties are more sensitive to changes in grain direction than others, e.g. tensile strength much more than strength in compression; practical advantage can often be taken of this – a beam placed with its major knots on the upper (compression) face is much stronger than if these defects were on the lower (tension) face, and particularly if they were near the middle of the span where the tensile stress is greatest.

Like other gels, wood stiffens on drying, and seasoned timber may have twice the strength of the wet wood, although against this increase may have to be set some loss due to splitting, loosening of knots and other forms of damage which may occur during seasoning.

For the design of timber structures in the past it has been usual to take average strength figures as determined by tests on small specimens clear of defects, and then to apply a safety factor of about 7 to cover contingencies including the possibility that the timber actually used may not be up to average. With the accumulation of more precise knowledge of the effect of knots, width of growth rings and other recognizable factors, and with an impetus derived from necessity, substantial economy is being achieved by taking these factors into account to assess the strength of each timber member more closely, in other words, by *stress-grading*.

In comparison with metals, on a weight for weight basis, seasoned wood, as a beam, has much higher strength, as would be expected from its hollow-tube cellular construction (which also accounts for its high thermal insulation qualities). Owing to its slightly plastic nature wood may be increasingly deformed by continuously applied loads and a sagging beam or shelf loaded near its maximum will fail in time. Plasticity is increased by steaming the wood and it can then be easily bent and on cooling and drying becomes set in its new shape.

The factors of interest to the wood anatomist which govern strength include the amount of wood substance present (i.e. density), its distribution, for example, whether fairly uniform or in sizeable aggregates of contrasting weak thin-walled and stronger thick-walled tissues, and lastly, its physico-chemical composition. As far as density is concerned the proportion of thick-walled fibres present has the principal effect, and this is roughly proportional in ring-porous hardwoods to the width of the growth rings; in diffuse-porous woods ring width has little effect on density, and in softwoods the proportion of thick-walled tracheids is higher in narrower rings. In all these classes rapidly grown wood is usually weak owing to the poor development of the fibre walls. These relationships are very approximate and are affected by the growing site and also, as shown by J. M.

Turnbull, by the age of the tree when the rings are formed. Accordingly, in judging the strength of a piece by inspection of its end-grain surface, it is preferable to consider the actual amount of dense fibrous tissue present than merely whether the rings are narrow or wide.

Most strength properties increase with density but some are much more closely related to it (e.g. resistance to compression) than others (e.g. toughness), depending apparently on the seat of initial failure. Compression fractures normally start in the body of the fibre walls, but impact fractures, as in toughness tests, which measure the ability of the wood to absorb a blow, start in the cementing layer between the cells and often amongst the relatively weak parenchyma so that, in this case, the strength of the fibre walls is not called upon.

With both compression strength and toughness, the two properties most closely studied, considerable variation occurs even with specimens of similar density and structure. That the reason for this lies in differences in the physico-chemical composition of the cell walls, apparently connected with their degree of lignification, was demonstrated by S. H. Clarke, using micro-chemical stains. Specimens of high compression strength for their density reacted strongly with the lignin-detecting stains, but such specimens were apt to be weak in toughness. Tropical hardwood timbers react more strongly with lignin stains and are stronger in compression but weaker in toughness for their weight than the timbers of temperate climates. These important differences in cell wall composition are clearly dependent on growth conditions, although the climatic or other factor responsible remains to be discovered; however it is significant that tropical species grown in temperate regions develop the properties and staining reaction characteristic of temperate species.

Durability. In considering the strength of any timber selected for a job the possibility must be recognised that some or all of its strength may be lost after a time owing to the ravages of micro-organisms or other pests, and appropriate preventive action taken. The risk varies according to the situation in which the timber is to be used; if it is kept continually wet, as in underwater piling, or permanently dry (at or below 20 per cent moisture content), as in furniture, then there is practically no risk of fungal decay since all wood-attacking fungi require both air and moisture. A partial exception is the Dry Rot fungus, which, once established on damp timber, may spread its growths to dry timber and exude sufficient moisture there to permit further attack.

The sapwood of all timbers is liable to fungal decay, but the coloured heartwood of many species (e.g. oak and larch) is naturally durable on account of their content of tannins and other slightly toxic substances formed during the transformation from sapwood. Some heavy dense timbers, although lacking such natural preservatives, may have a reasonable life when exposed to rot-inviting conditions (e.g. when partially embedded in the soil) owing to the large amount of wood substance present which must be destroyed by the fungi before the strength of the timber is seriously affected.

Wherever timber is to be used in exposed or damp situations protection by impregnation with creosote or other preservative is advisable. The general aim in such treatments is to ensure that the preservative is uniformly distributed in the outer portion of the timber to a depth beyond that which drying splits are likely to reach, say, $\frac{3}{4}$ inch; more complete impregnation is waste of expensive preservative and makes the timber unduly heavy. The sapwood of all species is readily permeable (especially along the grain) as would be expected in view of the conducting function the sapwood served in the tree up to the time of felling. Impregnation of softwoods is difficult owing to the fact that the bordered pits of softwoods become closed and sealed during the formation of heartwood; in some cases, e.g. Douglas fir sleepers, it is necessary to make numerous incisions in the surface to permit of adequate treatment. In hardwoods also the

heartwood is usually fairly impermeable; the vessels provide
the natural path for the preservative and in some species,
e.g. poplar, the other tissues are quite impermeable, while
in others which have the vessels blocked by tyloses, e.g.
English oak, the whole of the wood is practically impermeable. As some compensation for this, treatment is less
essential since well-developed heartwood has high natural
durability. However, this durability hardly equals that of
creosote-impregnated sapwood, and accordingly it is an
advantage to have sapwood on the exterior of timber which
is to be treated.

Impregnation with preservative protects timber not only
against fungi but also against insects, although it is not
commonly employed with this latter intention. Unlike the
fungi, many insect pests do not demand the presence of
moisture for their activities, as many a once-valuable piece
of worm-ridden furniture can bear witness. In this country
there are three kinds of insects which are chiefly responsible
for damage to seasoned timber, the Death-watch beetle
(*Xestobium rufovillosum*), the Common Furniture beetle
(*Anobium punctatum*) and the Powder-post beetle (*Lyctus*
spp.). The first of these derives its name from the ominous
ticking noise produced by the adults as a mating call by
tapping their heads on the surface of the timber. The cater-
pillar-like larva causes considerable damage by tunnelling
in old structural timbers, mainly oak; lack of ventilation,
dampness and previous attack by fungi predispose to this
form of attack. The common Furniture beetle larva,
responsible for the 'worm holes' seen in old roofing timbers, floors and furniture, is of more catholic taste and
attacks all kinds of wood, both sapwood and heartwood.
But the most destructive pest is the larva of the Powder-
post beetle, which attacks the freshly seasoned sapwood of
several valuable hardwoods, including oak, ash, walnut and
hickory. The female beetle when looking for vessels in which
to lay her eggs is careful to select sapwood which contains
starch, proved to be essential for the development of the

larva from the egg. Softwoods and those hardwoods having vessels too small to accommodate the eggs are neglected whether starch is present or not.

The starch-containing cells while alive normally use up some of their contents for respiration, and attempts have been made, with some success, to take advantage of this process to deplete the sapwood of its starch and so render it immune from attack by Powder-post beetle. The methods tried include cutting a girdle around the standing tree, just below the leafy crown, so as to sever the channels for downward passage of food materials which would otherwise replenish the starch respired away by the trunk. Another method is to keep the cells of the freshly-felled log alive and actively respiring by preventing them from drying out. A third method is to accelerate the respiration by warming the sawn timber in a seasoning kiln while at the same time maintaining a high humidity, so preventing drying out and the death of the respiring cells.

Final Remarks

In this brief article, largely written from the viewpoint of the biologist, it has been possible to give merely an introduction to the wide field covered by timber technology. Little or nothing has been said on many important aspects such as the rôle of wood structure in the identification of timbers, on woodworking, and the production of veneers, plywood and other composite materials, and for further information the reader is referred to the list of selected publications given below. It may also be noted that research on the fundamentals of wood, its growth and its properties, as well as the immediately practical problems involved in its utilization are continually in progress in Forest Products research laboratories and in Universities throughout the world. One of these practical problems concerns the revolution in the nature of its timber trade which post-war Britain has to face. Important former sources of supply have been closed and the many new timbers which have reached this

country as a result of the opening up of new forest areas or
the more intensive exploitation of old ones have produced the
numerous problems in utilization which inevitably arise
when there is no tradition to be invoked as a guide. Examination of the wood structure, in conjunction with the
accumulated fund of data on the relations between anatomy
and properties, is invaluable in the prompt assessment of
the qualities of these new timbers.

   To sum up, it may be said that a knowledge of the wood
structure makes possible a rational approach to an understanding of the properties of timber, and the problems
inherent in a raw material which shows the variation and
variety characteristic of organic products.

FURTHER READING

Bateson, R. G. (1938). *Timber Drying*. Crosby Lockwood, London.
Busgen, M., Münch, E., Thompson, T. (1929). *The Structure and Life
   of Forest Trees*. Chapman & Hall, London.
Clarke, S. H. (1939). *Recent Work on the Growth, Structure, and
   Properties of Wood*. Dept. Sci. & Ind. Res., Forest Products Res.
   Special Report No. 5. H.M. Stationery Office.
Desch, H. E. (1947). *Timber, its Structure and Properties*. 2nd Ed.
   Macmillan, London.
Forest Products Research Laboratory. *Publications on all aspects of
   timber technology*. H.M. Stationery Office.
Henderscn, F. Y. (1939). *Timber, its properties, pests, and preservation*.
   Crosby Lockwood, London.
Tiemann, H. D. (1942). *Wood Technology: constitution, properties and
   uses*. Pitman, New York.

The text figures and plates are reproduced by courtesy of the
Director, Forest Products Research Laboratory. (Crown copyright
reserved).

Vital Statistics of Fish Populations

G. L. KESTEVEN

Photogravure illustrations between pp. 64 and 65.

IN every fishery country of the world today where there is any development of modern science and technology and of modern ideas on administration, there is also a strong demand for scientific investigation of the fishery resources. Administrator and fisherman alike request thorough analysis of the fish populations and of all those factors by which the populations are affected. Both of them, administrator and fisherman, wish to know what quantities of fish may be taken from the fishing grounds by the fisherman's gear, and when and where and how that gear may be used; both of them are keenly aware of the necessity for proper management of the fish stocks, a management whose effect is recognised under the term 'conservation.' At one time this term had a limited meaning, being generally understood to indicate the measures adopted to restrict (unpleasantly it was held) the operations of fishermen upon stocks which had become depleted, and in this way to restore the strength of those stocks. But it is now recognised that the same methods of investigation and the same measures for administration should be applied to all fisheries with the objective of securing the wisest and most effective exploitation* of these stocks: conservation now is accepted as meaning the whole programme devised for these ends.

A fisheries management plan involves two, generally

*Even this word has had a chequered career: primarily its verb was used to mean 'to achieve' and then 'to turn to account'; subsequently it was used to mean 'to utilise for selfish purposes.'

simultaneous, programmes, of research and of administration. The latter may in the beginning work by commonsense and first principles, but it looks to the former to prepare specific rules for the continued conduct of the fishery: in precise terms, administration expects to be told the quantities of fish which may be taken year by year from the stocks, the lower limits in respect of size of fish to be taken, any limitations upon the use of gear in respect of time or place or design, and other general information. This can be done by the investigators, in the course of time. Their programme falls into three principal phases: there is a first exploratory phase in which the general limits of distribution and the major features of the biology of the stock are defined; during the second phase the precise population characteristics of the stock are evaluated, and the third phase is a continuing one (corresponding in many respects to the activities of meteorological bureaux) in which the investigators advise administration, and the industry, of variations in the stock from year to year.

The Optimum Catch

The first question is 'what is the greatest catch we may take from this stock of fish, this year and next year and in each year thereafter, remembering that as a nation we want to be able to take those quantities for ever – or at least while men will want fish for food?' Among fishery biologists the catch, from any stock, which conforms to these requirements is known as the optimum catch. It is called the best because not only does it not cause any depletion but allows of fishing operations for ever, but also it has the beneficial effect of ensuring greatest production by the stock. It is possible for the fishermen to take too few fish: in fact that is what happened in natural conditions, and in such a case the population is an aged one with a greater proportion of old fish than is desirable. Where this happens there is overcrowding of the grounds, and the growth rate of the individual fish is reduced. On the other hand it is possible, as is well known, to take too many fish, so that the stocks become depleted and the population juvenile. The optimum catch is the middle way, the desirable mean. The effect of fishing operations on a fishing ground which has never been worked before must be likened to thinning a forest: there is a reduction of the population density, some of the giant individuals are removed and the younger ones have a better opportunity to grow, there being more food and space available to each individual. These effects will probably continue at all times, but as the population becomes more and more reduced the effects will become weaker and weaker, and at the same time will be offset by other, unfavourable effects. The principal unfavourable effect is the reduction in the capacity of the stocks to produce young and in this way to secure the maintenance of the population. It will be clear of course that whilst maturity is reached at different ages by different organisms, there is for every species a minimum age at which maturity is achieved; further, it has been shown for fish that the fecundity of each individual (that is, the number of eggs which each can produce in a season) increases as the fish grows older. Thus, if fishing operations are excessive, not only will the actual number of spawners be reduced but, since their average age will become less and less, their total fecundity will diminish.

It will be seen that the whole of this problem is a population one: how many individuals are there and what is the density of the population, how many are there of each sex, and how many of each age? Moreover, what variation is there from year to year in the answer to these questions? The resemblance of these questions to those which motivate a census of a human population will be apparent, and in fact the tasks are very similar but the methods are greatly different, which will be easily recognised. For one thing a census of fish is made by indirect methods which rather resemble those adopted by 'mass observation' observers, or what you would get if you stood at the entrance to a metropolitan railway station and interrogated every third or fourth (or other) individual as to his or her age, occupation and so forth and used these results as applicable to the entire population. But it is even more difficult since you cannot observe your population naturally; in forestry and other botanical work it is possible to view the whole population even though you examine in detail only small sections of it, but this is not available to the fishery investigator who has access, in the main, only to samples, i.e. to commercial and experimental catches. A partial exception exists in the case of salmon fisheries where a large part of the population is observed when it passes through counting chambers which close off the passage upstream.

In the following pages it is intended to give a brief account of the problems and the methods of carrying out a census of natural fish populations for the purpose of stating the optimum catch for the benefit of administration.

Fish Populations

We shall for reasons of convenience, distinguish between the characteristics of a fish population and its properties. By the former we mean its distribution, numerical strength and density, and its sex and age composition. The latter include its potentials of growth and reproduction and its mortalities. This corresponds to the difference of form and function between anatomy and physiology; the characteristics of the population are its form or structure and its properties are its capacity for function or change.

Distribution: Racial Investigations

The distribution of a species of fish is established in approximate terms, from reports of fishermen, both professional (or commercial) and amateur, and from the collections made by investigators. Much of this work was already done by the end of the nineteenth century: that century having been distinguished by the number of outstanding oceanographic expeditions, in the course of which considerable additions were made to our knowledge of marine life. However, for work of the kind described here, it is necessary to have precise definition of the limits of distribution, not only of each species but also of each distinct unit of population, or stock, of each species; moreover, whilst the broad outlines of the distribution of a particular species might be known, there are important details in respect of the distribution of life-phases within those outlines, which must be clarified. These problems have been attacked by a number of methods. One of these is to prepare very precise descriptions of the different groups within a species and to compare these descriptions to ascertain whether there is any permanent difference between them. Thus in the case of the herring of the North Sea and adjacent waters: whilst the general distribution of the species is known it is suspected that a number of races exists within the area and that these in some cases intermingle whilst in others they remain quite distinct and are separate all their life. In an effort to discover whether such races do exist and what their distribution might be within the species-limit, many workers have examined tremendous numbers of herring in very close detail; these workers have found certain differences in the number of segments in the vertebral column and in the number of keeled scales along the ventral edge of the body; other anatomical features have been measured or counted but have been shown to vary little. There has been extensive argument on the value of the differences observed for showing distinct races. Physiological features may also vary and reveal the existence of races.

From the anatomical method of racial determination (as these investigations are called), we can turn to the experimental technique of tagging operations: these have now been used successfully on practically every major kind of fish. For want of better term the word *tagging* is used to include the technique, used on salmon, of marking fish by some mutilation of the fish – such as removing adipose fins (these are fins which have no bony skeleton). Tagging proper (Plate 23) consists of attaching a metal or plastic label to some part of the animal, or of inserting such a label; these labels usually carry lettering by which the tagging operation is identified, and there is usually also a number by which the particular fish is identified. The essential difference between tagging proper and the technique of mutilation, is that a mutilation cannot do more than identifiy very generally the place and perhaps time at which the fish was tagged: a label identifies the particular fish, and this permits not only more precise indication of the time and place of release, but also some measurement of the growth of the individual fish in the interval of absence. Experiments of this kind have been carried out on cod, plaice, lemon soles, halibut, salmon, herrings, sardines and

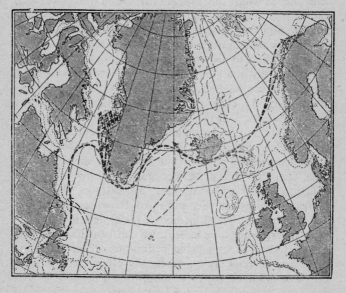

Fig. 1—Migrations. Some long-range migrations of cod marked at the spawning grounds of South Iceland. (*From A. Vedel Taning, by permission of the Conseil International pour l'Exploration de la Mer.*)

numerous other species. The cod marking work has revealed very extensive migrations by cod and shown exchanges between the different stocks of the North Atlantic (Fig. 1). The work on halibut established the fact that there was a number of distinct units of population which were quite separate and which must be treated independently in any programme of management. Similar results were obtained from the tagging operations on the Pacific herring where the population units are much more restricted. On the other hand, a close ally of this herring, the California sardine, migrates into Canadian waters and back.

These results have a very great effect on the research programme and also on the plans for administration, since these must be concerned in every case with the total population. Considerable confusion can arise where the investigators, under the impression that they are working on a distinct unit of population, are in effect overlooking exchanges between the population with which they are working and some other neighbouring population. Such effects can invalidate an entire set of biological conclusions.

Composition of the Population
The sex-composition of the population is fairly easily determined, for it involves simply a large amount of field work in examining the gonads of fish.* It has been found that the ratio of males to females is a fairly constant feature of each species; there are perhaps exceptions, as for instance in some eels, where it is suggested that there is some hermaphroditism and sex-change and the proportion of males to females changes substantially. There are some characteristic segregations of the sexes in certain species and this could have very considerable effect on the population where mortality and other effects operated differentially upon the segregations. Segregations such as this have to be looked for in the investigations and allowed for in working out the properties of the population.

* i.e. the roe ; 'hard roe' is ovary and 'soft roe' testis.

Much work has been carried out by fisheries biologists in determining the age of fish and in analysing the age composition of fish stocks. There are three principal methods of carrying out this work. In the Peterson method a graph is made of the fish taken in a particular place at a particular time; in this graph the number of fish at each length are plotted, giving a picture such as in Fig. 2. Such

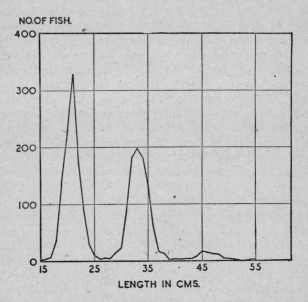

Fig. 2—Length frequency diagram for haddock. This figure shows clearly the 'peaks' which indicate age-groups—in this case fish of approximately 1½, 2½, and 3½ years of age. (*Drawn from data of H. Thompson.*)

a diagram reveals peaks, or modes, which represent the major groups within the population; after extended biological investigations it is often possible to identify such groups as representing aggregations of individuals of the same age – that is, they are age groups, each group the product of one breeding season. By a combination of biology, geometry and statistics it is possible to make a dissection of a series of such curves so as to prepare a picture of the age composition of the population. This method has been employed in the case of the North Sea cod and also for the California sardine.

The other two methods of age determination (and of composition analysis) are those employing the marks on scales and on otoliths.* The methods are essentially the same. Both structures (in those species in which the method can be employed) carry annuli, *i.e.* growth-rings, corresponding in many respects to the growth-rings in the trunks of trees, representing the years of life of the fish (Plate 24). It is unnecessary to go into the details of structure, or into the difficulties of interpretation of many of the scales (and otoliths) on which work has been performed. It is sufficient to say that the method is valid and permits of a reasonably accurate estimate of the age of individual fish of certain species, and analysis of the age composition of samples of such fish. This work has been carried out on many thousands of fish in the investigations of fisheries biology; it has been used for the North Sea herring, for salmon, the haddock and many other species.

Just as a graph for length against frequency is prepared for the Peterson method, similarly a graph for age against frequency is prepared in the case of determination of age from scales or otoliths. Work of this kind has revealed very great differences in the composition of populations of the same species, as between different years and between different localities. These differences are the result of the operation of numerous factors relating to the nutrition, the destruction of various age groups and the capacity for reproduction.

One of the most distinctive features of fish biology, and one which was earliest observed, was the existence of wide variations in the abundance of the fish. In some years the

*'Ear-stones,' masses of calcium carbonate secreted in the inner ear.

fish of a particular species were found in large quantities,
and then in other years there would be relatively few of
them (Fig. 3). Sometimes these periods of abundance (or

Fig. 3—Changes in the abundance
of fish. Numbers of cod caught off
the coast of Norway in different years
(*From Johan Hjort, by permission of
the Conseil International pour l'Exploration de la Mer.*)

of scarcity) persisted for a number of years, sometimes there
was a general average level of abundance with exceptional
years of great or little abundance. The investigations of
this phenomenon of fluctuating abundance have shown
that it may fall into one or other of two major classes: there
may be changes in *accessibility*, or changes in the *actual
abundance* of the fish. The former occurs in the case of
migrating fish whose movements are subject to physical
and chemical factors within the water: thus the movements

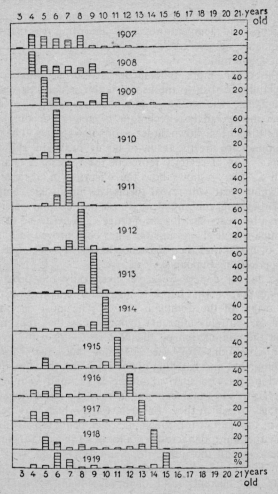

Fig. 4—Age composition of herring stocks. It will be seen how the brood from a particular year can predominate. Thus there is a strong 4-year old class in 1908 which appears strongly each year thereafter. (of course becoming older) until 1919. (*From Johan Hjort, by permission of the Conseil International pour l'Exploration de la Mer.*)

of mackerel off the Norwegian coast are controlled by
currents and temperatures and according to these the
abundance of mackerel available to the Norwegian fishermen is determined.

The other, more fundamental cause of difference in
availability of fish to the fishery is the actual difference in
abundance. The nature of this phenomenon was revealed
when the age-analysis technique became an accomplished
fact. It has been shown, at least for some species, that years
of abundance are the result of highly successful spawning
years: years of scarcity represent the reverse. A diagram
such as Fig. 4 shows how the offspring of a successful
spawning year will reveal themselves in an age-composi-
tion diagram, entering strongly on the left and persisting
year after year until lost in old age. The existence of such
dominant year-classes in stocks has been proved in a number of cases, and their existence has been associated with
the periods of abundance.

So far of course we have given only the proximate
explanation of what happens: there still remains to explain
the origin of the dominant classes. The most reasonable
(and an entirely sufficient) hypothesis is that they result
from the conjunction of adequate spawners with favourable conditions for the spawning act, the survival,
development and hatching of the eggs, and the subsequent
development and survival of the larvae and young fish.
The hazards to which eggs and larvae are subject, including
enemies by which they are eaten, water which may be too
hot or too cold or too rough, or which being too swift may
carry them into dangerous conditions or disperse them too
widely, are all too numerous. Some fascinating work has
been done on the distribution of eggs and larvae by surface
drifts and currents, and their consequent survival and
destruction.

Variations in the intensity of fishing operations, related
as they are to economic factors, play a substantial part in
the changes in catch and have not been overlooked in these

investigations. The fluctuations referred to here are those which remain after allowances have been made for technological and economic factors.

The Properties of Fish Populations

The properties in which we are interested in fish populations are the potentials for growth and reproduction. There may be innumerable other properties which might be of interest, but it is these two more than others which concern us, since they determine the ability of the population to sustain fishing operations and thus serve as a resource for human exploitation. The properties of the population are the sum total of the properties of the individuals of which it is composed, and we must therefore begin with the individual.

The growth of individual fish can rarely be directly observed, but the methods by which the age of the fish can be determined can be employed in measuring the growth of groups of fish and also of individual fish. Thus, if the mean length of the fish at each successive age can be determined, then a new diagram, as in Fig. 5, can be prepared to

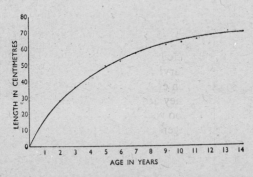

Fig. 5—Growth of fish. Mean lengths plotted against age. (*Drawn from data of H. Thompson.*)

show the normal growth of the fish. On the other hand, it has been shown, with reservations, that there is a relationship (in those species in which scale and otolith reading is practicable) between the growth of the scale (or otolith) and the growth of the fish, so that for each species a scale of a given size corresponds (within limits) to a fish of certain size; therefore, if one takes a scale from a fish which is say three years and a few months old, as revealed by the scale, and measures not only the whole diameter of the scale but also the diameters to the edge of the successive rings, then applying to each of the other diameters in turn the ratio 'the whole scale diameter to the length of the fish when captured,' one obtains the length which the fish had at the end of each of those years (Plate 24). Although various precautions must be exercised in applying this technique, it does yield reliable results which can give a

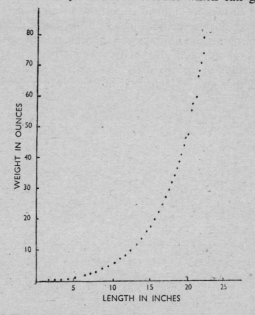

Fig. 6—The relation between the weight and the length of mullet. (*From G. L. Kesteven.*)

more detailed account of the growth of the fish. Particularly, these results permit an analysis of the differences of success of growth by different fish, in different localities and different years, and these can in turn be related to the factors determining growth. Such analyses, carried out on a number of species, reveal that the amount of growth may vary very considerably as between individuals, localities, seasons and years and is dependent upon such factors as population density, availability of food and the conditions in the sea. These results are of greatest importance in relation to the optimum catch since what is wanted is *weight* of catch rather than numbers of fish. The measurement of the total growth potential of fish populations has not proceeded far in fisheries biology.

Practically all of these investigations have been concerned with the growth of some linear dimension, generally the total length or some major proportion of that. Parallel investigations of the growth in weight corresponding to various increments of length have also been pursued on smaller numbers of fish. These investigations yield a graph like that in Fig. 6. Further these investigations reveal differences in the amount of weight corresponding to similar lengths; this technique has been employed extensively by amateur investigators of salmon and trout who calculate an index called the condition factor which in general consists of multiplying the cube of the length of the fish by some factor and then dividing by the weight of the fish. The variations in the index are said to measure variations in the conditions which affect the growth of the fish: it is probable that although this section of the programme has not been extensively employed in fishery investigations, it will develop and become very effective in the future.

The second potential in which we are interested is the reproductive. The relationship of fecundity to length (and age) is similar to that between weight and length: that is to say, the larger (and older) the fish, the greater is its capacity to produce eggs, and thereby to contribute offspring to

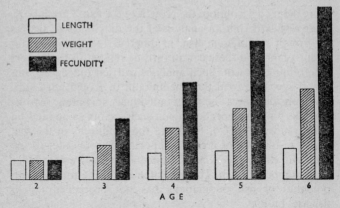

Fig. 7—The relationship between age, length, weight and fecundity.
*From Raitt, by permission of the Conseil International pour l'Exploration
de la Mer.)*

the population (Fig. 7). It will be recognised that, having
an analysis of the age composition of the population, knowing the 'condition' of each age group and also the fecundity
of each age group, then the total reproductive capacity can
be calculated. The extension of these results to the entire
population is a matter of some difficulty which we shall
consider after making a brief examination of the question
of mortality.

The force which opposes the tendency of the population
to expand by its growth and reproduction potentials is,
of course, mortality. It is presumed that under natural
conditions the two sets of forces exist in a kind of flexible
balance, such that a swing to either side of the level of
average abundance will be followed immediately by a com-
pensating swing to the opposite side. When the population
becomes subject to fishing operations some weight is thrown
into the repressive side and, unless precautions are taken,
the balance will be irrevocably depressed on the debit side
with an inevitable decline. As in the case of the characteristics of the population the mortalities can be known only

indirectly. They appear, in a crude form, in the rate of diminution of relative numbers of each particular age group in the population. This will be seen from the following figures borrowed from some work on haddock. The table shows the relative abundance of each age group of the population of North Sea haddock, as revealed year by year in research fishing. Those fish which are shown as 2nd year in 1923 (of which there were 330) are the same brood as the 3rd year (390) in 1924, the 4th year (160) in 1925, and so on. Each brood (that is the offspring of each year) is to be followed through this table in this way. It will be seen that in some cases there is an increase between the 2nd and 3rd year and thereafter a decline.

NORTH SEA HADDOCK.

Average number of each age-class caught (research vessel) per 100 hours fishing. (Thompson, 1930).

	Age Group					
	Second	Third	Fourth	Fifth	Sixth	Seventh
In 1923	330	1,720	9.090	1,310	200	70
1924	28,060	390	860	4,100	820	150
1925	11,920	23,860	160	300	1,490	590
1926	9,640	11,530	8,510	130	300	640
1927	15,240	6,670	4,640	3,530	100	230
1928	2,920	15,990	2,170	1,250	590	30

The rates represented here could be accepted as representing accurately the conditions in the natural population only if it were known that the samples from which such rates were calculated held a precise relationship with the natural stocks. It is generally true that a precise relationship does not exist: samples are taken with all manner of bias, special selection is inevitably made from special aggregations of the population, special age groups, special racial groups, special sex groups are continually intervening. It is extremely difficult to obtain any assurance that each of the age, sex and other groups is represented in the samples exactly in the proper relative strengths as they exist in the natural population. One of the major tasks of fisheries research is to procure such exactitude of relationship. In this task use is made of a number of devices of which the tagging technique is particularly successful. It is permissible to argue that if so many tagged individuals are released into a stable population and if subsequently in the course of normal fishing operations some proportion of these tagged individuals is recovered in company with so many individuals without tags, then the three figures – number tagged, number of tagged fish recovered, number of non-tagged fish taken – permit of a calculation from which the number of individuals in the stable population may be estimated; it is a matter of proportions. Again it is unnecessary to describe the necessary precautions in applying this technique. On the other hand, even if a calculation such as this cannot be made, the returns of recovered tagged fish serve, with due precautions, to show the rate at which the fish are being taken by the fishing operations. Then if the rate at which fishing is removing the fish from the population is known, we are in a position to make an analysis of the gross figures of rates of decline of particular year groups. In this way we are able to reach some understanding of the causes which are responsible for the mortality in the population.

Mortality curves in fish may possibly, in the natural state, resemble those of human beings, with maxima early and late in life and a minimum at some intermediate point. However, no comprehensive curve is available for any species yet. What we know is that the rate of mortality is very considerable in the first weeks of life, and this has actually been measured in a few instances; also the rate in some other years is known approximately. That these rates are extremely variable from year to year, and between particular year-groups in any one calendar year, is fairly clear from results to date.

Total Numbers
So far we have spoken in the main of various rates of growth

and reproduction and of mortality, and we have suggested that by tagging operations the numbers in a parent population may become known. There are really many ways in which the various sets of data already described can be incorporated and employed in an estimate of the actual abundance of the fish population.

One method consists of estimating the number of eggs (of the species under consideration) which are spawned into the sea within a limited area; since the average number of eggs spawned by each individual is also known, the division of the one figure into the other gives an estimate of the total number of spawners in the area. Knowing also the ratio of spawners to the remainder of the stock, the total numbers of the stock can be estimated. This method has been used in the North Sea for plaice, and in the West Atlantic for mackerel.

Another method is that, referred to previously, involving the use of tags. Under certain conditions the number of returned tags can be used, in relation to the number of untagged fish taken at the same time, as the basis to an estimate of the numbers in the population into which the tags were released.

The tagging technique enters a further set of methods based on the argument that if accurate measurement is made of various ratios such as mortality rates, and if one of the proportionals can be measured absolutely, then the other proportionals can also become known. Thus, if the biological analysis can reveal the total mortality rate, and if further methods such as tagging can reveal the proportion which fishing mortality is of the total, then, since the quantity which is taken by fishing is known from standard statistical records, the total quantity of mortality can become known. And since, further, the mortality is known as a rate, then the numbers of the population can become known.

It must not be supposed that these methods are easy of application: they are in fact difficult and involved, requir-

ing a vast amount of information and a persistent search for
disturbing factors for which allowance must be made. It
will be recognised that one of the most important pre-
requisites is a precise definition of the limits of distribution
of the population being assessed: useful results cannot be
expected from work which is based on a section only of a
population, such that there is constant but unmeasured
movement into and out of this section in exchanges with
other sections.

FURTHER READING.

Hjort, Johan. *Human Value of Biology* (Cambridge, Mass., 1938),
(gives an account of some of the methods of fisheries research and of
the importance of such work to fisheries).

Russell, E. S. *The Overfishing Problem* (Cambridge, 1942) (contains
an admirable exposition of the modern theory of fisheries).

Graham, M. *The Fish Gate* (London, 1943) (an excellent account of
the problems of the fishing industry and of the methods of fisheries
work).

Milk: its Formation and Secretion

F. H. MALPRESS

THAT "Every man adopts to food, a scientific attitude" must be deemed, even in these days of enlightenment, a bold overstatement, but the importance of milk from the nutritional standpoint is a matter upon which few people would now prove completely ignorant. Two European wars coming at a time when the study of biochemistry was attracting an ever greater interest among scientists, have inevitably resulted in particular attention being given to the nature of foodstuffs, the composition of dietaries and the results which might be expected from an insufficient or inadequate food intake, and from the start milk has figured prominently in such investigations. Somewhat belatedly, perhaps, this knowledge is being made available to the public at large through a number of popular channels and every housewife now knows that of all single foods milk is the most complete; that although it is mostly water it contains in amounts adequate enough for the early development of her baby, a carbohydrate – lactose – which is readily convertible to energy, fats which provide a store of energy and also act as a solvent for valuable vitamins, and proteins of very good type which are well able to carry out their major role in the formation of new non-skeletal tissue. Also that it has a high content of mineral salts, of which calcium and phosphorus – both essential for skeletal growth and therefore of paramount importance in the dietaries of young children – are particularly important. The advice she receives on supplementing her baby's ration will suggest, too, that complete though it is as a food-stuff, milk has certain faults,

notably inadequate amounts of iron and of some of the
vitamins, for which other provision must therefore be made.

Although the importance of milk in the diet naturally
decreases as the baby grows and other less easily digestible
foods can be utilized, we might note that sufficient energy
could be gained for the needs of an adult living on a milk
diet alone, provided he drank about a gallon of milk a day,
an amount which – could he accomplish such a feat –
would ensure him an abundance of the other chief food
constituents as well. This decline in the significance of milk
in the dietary of the growing animal does not therefore cast
a reflection upon the value of milk as an adult food, but
is merely a limitation made at the dictates of convenience
and epicurism, and in acceptance of the fact that there are
virtues in the mere slowly-digesting bulkiness of more
solid foods. The qualitative merit of milk as a food goes
unchallenged for all men at all ages.

Complementary to the investigation of the nutritional
worth of milk there is the study of its production and secretion by the mammal, and although there is a great deal still
to be discovered in this field of inquiry and much that is
controversial, it provides the facts with which this article
is mainly concerned.

Quite clearly, before milk can be produced at all, milk-
secretory tissue has to be present, and although existing in
rudimentary form in the young immature animal, such
tissue only achieves functional significance under normal
conditions following the action of certain stimuli associated
with pregnancy, the development of the mammary glands
and the phenomenon of lactation being in the physiological
sense indispensable phases of the mammalian reproductive
process.

Before considering the nature of the control of mammary
growth it will be well to allay a possible confusion which
might arise from the use of the word "gland" in the text
with different connotations. First, there is the popular usage
of the word which has reference to certain centres of lymph-

atic tissue such as the tonsils, and to which we refer when we talk of "swollen glands"; these are primarily concerned with countering infection in the body and will not further interest us here. A more pertinent confusion may be present when we speak on the one hand of mammary and sweat glands and on the other of the endocrine glands such as the thyroid, the gonads or sex glands, and the pituitary. We might characterise these last two groupings as glands of external and internal secretion respectively. The first group, including the mammary glands, all elaborate their own specific secretions which are external in that, like milk or sweat, they are exuded on to the body surfaces. They may be nutritive like milk, lubricative or protective, but are not marked by any power to affect other physiological processes in the organism. The *endocrine glands* on the other hand are all characterised by just this power to influence in the most far-reaching ways the development and functioning of the organism from which they themselves derive. Their secretions contain biologically active substances called *hormones* which are poured directly from the gland into the circulating blood stream, and so are enabled to cause generalised systemic reactions, or alternatively to exert their effects upon other tissues remote from the site of their own formation. It will be understood therefore in what follows that, particularly in the nature and disposal of its secretory products, the mammary gland is quite distinct from those glands of internal secretion which, as we shall see, control its development and functioning.

Development of the Mammary Gland

If we except the egg-laying mammals such as the duck-billed platypus, whose mammary tissue shows a more primitive structure than that of the viviparous mammals, the mammary glands whether of the rat or man, of cow or monkey have the same double structure: the alveoli, which are the actual secretory organs, consisting of groups of specialised cells arranged spherically round a central lumen, and the ducts which are the collecting channels through which the formed milk passes to the teat or nipple. The ducts unite and get progressively larger as they get nearer the teat, so that the complete structure of alveoli and ducts

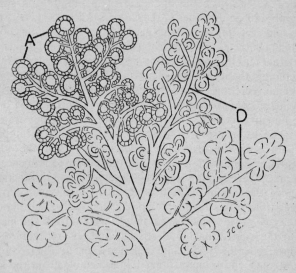

Fig. 1—Sectional diagrammatic representation of mammary structures (greatly enlarged). A, alveoli; D, ducts.

may be likened to a bunch of grapes. (Fig. 1). Of course the fine cellular structure of the alveoli, or indeed the alveoli themselves, can only be observed with the aid of a microscope, but the outline of the general arborescence can be well seen with the naked eye in the glands of some small mammals such as the rat, whose mammary tissue – unlike the localised, "three-dimensional" form of the human breast or the cow's udder – spreads widely in a thin layer over the ventral surface of the animal's body.

In conformity with the structural similarity of the glands the mechanisms underlying mammary growth are also very nearly the same for all mammals; and these mechanisms are hormonal and not nervous. In other words they depend upon the action of secretions of the endocrine glands upon the undeveloped mammary pad, notably the secretions of the ovary and of the pituitary. It was fairly simple to disprove the earlier belief in a nervous control of mammary growth. Two obvious experiments could be performed; the cutting of all nervous pathways to the mammary site, or the transplantation of mammary tissue, freed of its nervous connections, to another part of the body. If under such denervated conditions the tissues were still observed to develop in an ensuing pregnancy – as actually was the case – then control by nervous impulse of the growth of alveoli and ducts could clearly be ruled out and a different mechanism sought.

Gradually there has been built up a picture in which the ovarian hormones – the oestrogens and progesterone – are seen to occupy positions of primary importance in this control. It may be noted here that these hormones of the female sex-gland besides their role in mammary growth play important parts in the development of other female sex characteristics, the various changes associated with puberty, including the onset of the menstrual flow, being correlated with the awakening activity of the ovaries at this time and the start of oestrogen and progesterone secretion; moreover they are together responsible for certain proliferative changes in the uterus, essential for the embedding of the fertilised ovum in the early stages of pregnancy, and play a role in the provision of suitable conditions for the continuation of foetal growth until birth.

In so far as the mammary gland is concerned it is believed that the oestrogens promote duct growth, and that in combination with progesterone they cause the development of the alveoli; but there are species differences which for the moment preclude the full acceptance of this generalisation. Particularly is this so for alveolar growth, which in some species – the guinea-pig for example – would seem to result from oestrogenic action alone. However it may well prove

that qualitatively the stimuli required are identical for all
mammals, such variations as are observed being of a quantitative character only. Since then, for most species,
progesterone may be considered essential for alveolar
growth, and since it is only during pregnancy that this
hormone is present in large amounts in the circulation of
the normal animal, it follows that it is only at this time that
conditions will be favourable for the development of the
secretory cells. The post-pubertal development of the mammary glands observed in the human and some other
mammals, is due – in so far as true glandular elements are
involved – to the slow extension of the duct system alone
at this time, under the action of ovarian oestrogen; while
the process of weaning at the end of lactation is associated
with the regression of alveolar cells formed during pregnancy and the resumption of a simple duct development. It
is only therefore during the latter half of pregnancy and the
period of lactation following birth of the young, that the
mammary glands of most species can be regarded as structurally complete. At all other times alveolar tissue is absent
in any quantity, and lactation could only be produced after
first stimulating both the growth of the secretory cells and
the enlargement of the existing duct system by suitable
injections of the ovarian hormones.

Recently the simple theory of ovarian control of mammary growth (Fig. 2a) has been complicated by a suggestion
that what was hitherto thought to be a direct action of the

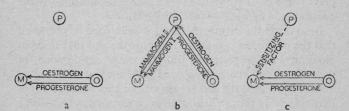

Fig. 2—Diagrammatic representation of three theories of mammary
growth control. P, pituitary; O, ovary; M, mammary gland.

ovarian hormones on the mammary gland is in fact an indirect action involving a prior stimulation of the pituitary by these hormones. Parenthetically we may note here that the pituitary is a small gland at the base of the brain. It has many functions and in particular it secretes a number of hormones which directly influence the plane of activity of other endocrine glands. It is sometimes referred to therefore as a "master-gland," and although this term does not by any means tell the whole story of pituitary function, it emphasises conveniently one of its most important roles. Structurally the gland shows division into two main parts – the anterior and posterior lobes – both of which are concerned in the control of lactation: the anterior lobe in the formation and secretion of milk (lactogenic action, q.v.) and possibly in the development of mammary tissue (mammogenic action, v. inf.); the posterior lobe in the ejection of milk from the gland (oxytocic action, q.v.).

The more elaborate theory of mammary growth which has been put forward – the "mammogenic theory" – postulates the secretion of two pituitary hormones – mammogens I and II – and suggests that it is these substances which are directly responsible for the growth observed. It will be appreciated however that the ovarian hormones still retain their position as the ultimate initiators of the response, since it is they that stimulate mammogen release from the pituitary (Fig. 2b). The matter is still one for debate, even though claims have been put forward for the isolation of the two mammogens. A third hypothesis, more recent still, and one that does not recognise the arguments of the mammogenic theory, supposes that although oestrogens and progesterone act directly on the mammary gland, their action is dependent upon a state of pre-sensitization in the gland, induced by the pituitary (Fig. 2c).

To choose between three hypotheses so closely allied is no simple matter for the physiologist, for experiments which might lead to a critical assessment of their accuracy almost inevitably involve techniques – such as the removal

of the pituitary gland – which impose flagrantly artificial
conditions upon the experimental animals concerned, and
in so doing render suspect any conclusions which may be
drawn from them. The riddle remains therefore unanswered
but, so far as we know, with three possible answers.

Control of Milk Secretion

Whatever the role of the pituitary gland may prove to be
in the control of mammary growth, there can be no doubt
of its pre-eminent part in the promotion and maintenance
of secretory activity in the mammary tissue once it has been
laid down. It provides a fine example of the dovetailing of
physiological processes that lactation should be withheld,
even though the mammary gland is fully formed, until the
time of parturition. The impulses that govern its timely
onset after the birth of the young are again hormonal in
character – a sudden drop, of complex origin, in the concentration of oestrogen in the blood stream at this time,
and as a consequence – and this is the important thing for
us to notice in this context – the removal of the inhibitory
effect which this hormone has, when present in high concentrations, upon the secretion of a group of pituitary
hormones known as the pituitary lactogens. The formation
and release of these lactogens is very sensitive to different
concentrations of oestrogens in the circulating blood; if

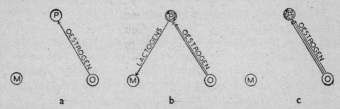

Fig. 3—Diagrammatic representation of the effect of increasing
blood oestrogen concentrations (a <b <c) on the secretion of pituitary
lactogens. a, unstimulated; b, stimulated; c, inhibited. P, pituitary
(cross-hatching indicates the presence of lactogen); O, ovary; M,
mammary gland.

the concentration is raised above a certain level their formation and release are inhibited, even though, on analysis,
the pituitary gland itself might be found to contain a high
lactogen concentration (Fig. 3c); at lower concentrations
there would seem to be a range in which this inhibition gives
way to an actual stimulation of the secretions (Fig. 3b).
This clearly will be the range essential for milk production.
At lower concentrations still there is no action at all –
whether inhibitory or stimulatory – and lactogen secretion
may be regarded as absent (Fig. 3a). This effect, dependent
on quantitative changes alone, while accounting satis-
factorily for the mechanism of onset of lactation at term,
can also provide an explanation for such opposed effects
of the oestrogens as their ability to stop the flow of milk in a
lactating animal and to initiate it in a dry one. The clarify-
ing concept is that of the differential action of the oestrogens
on the pituitary gland when present in high and low concentrations in the blood.

That the hormones causing mammary alveolar tissues to
secrete are of pituitary origin was first demonstrated in 1928
when lactation was induced in rabbits having fully formed
but non-lactating glands, by the simple process of injecting
them with aqueous pituitary extracts. The assumption at
first was that one hormone alone – prolactin – was responsible for the initiation of the secretory processes, but
gradually it has become more likely that prolactin is only
one of a group of pituitary hormones sharing, each in its
own way, this control. This multiplicity of lactogenic power
was first seen clearly when purified preparations of prolactin were found inferior to more crude pituitary preparations,
of equal prolactin content, in their power to increase the
milk yield of cows already lactating. A distinction has also
been drawn between lactogenesis – the power of initiating
milk secretion – and galactopoiesis – the power of maintaining the flow of milk once it has been started. It seems
possible, however, that the same hormones are concerned in
both these processes, and that there are merely quantitative

changes in the balance of importance held between the
hormones of the group themselves as lactation passes
through the successive phases of initiation, colostrum
secretion, peak yield and decline. In any case, whatever
the composition of the lactogenic and galactopoietic com-
plexes proves to be, and whether they are identical or different, there can be no doubt that it is the pituitary gland which
first and foremost governs the processes of milk-secretion
from the alveoli.

From the very fact that milk is such a complex fluid,
however, it is clear that we must be prepared to visualise
the combined processes of its formation and secretion as
being very complex too. For instance, all the major constituents of milk are specific, so far as the organism is
concerned, for this fluid alone. The typical protein – casein –
occurs nowhere else in the body; nor does the milk-sugar,
lactose, or the milk fat – butter. This means that the
alveolar cell must be the seat of intense biochemical activity,
the medium of many complicated metabolic conversions,
and it is not surprising therefore that we should find many
other hormones, apart from those of the pituitary gland,
appearing to exert very appreciable effects upon the character and level of milk secretion. This, however, does not
necessarily imply that they have any specific action on the
alveolar cells, as is the case with pituitary lactogens; rather,
their effects may be the result of more generalised activities
such as can frequently be ascribed to hormones; for
example, effects on the permeability of cells to ions and
other dissolved substances, or on the mobilisation from
other parts of the body of "precursors" – the starting
materials for the biochemical conversions taking place in
the gland. On the other hand, and more specifically, the
action might be on the progress of these conversions themselves once they are under way. Hormonal action along any
of these lines might influence the rate of milk-secretion very
considerably by affecting indirectly the working efficiency
of the alveolar cell. It is almost certain that the lactogenic

action of the thyroid hormone is attributable to some such non-specific influence, while that of some of the hormones of the adrenal gland may eventually be explained on similar grounds.

It will be appreciated then that although the broad out-lines of the control of milk secretion are now fairly well understood, and we can in many cases ascribe definite physiological changes to individual hormones, we are sadly at a loss when we seek to go one stage further in our inquiries and interpret these changes in biochemical or biophysical terms. What is the mode of action of the lacto-genic hormones upon the alveolar cell? To say that they stimulate it to secrete milk is to give a reply in purely functional terms which, by itself, is unsatisfactory; for there lie, unexplained and hidden behind such a statement, facts of more fundamental importance which when brought to light will allow us to understand function in terms of the influences exerted on metabolic processes. At present the endocrinologist talks almost exclusively in terms of func-tion; but inevitably he must think more and more of the integration of hormonal action with metabolic change if he is to put his studies in their true perspective. An example has already been set by the comparatively recent bio-chemical approach to the study of vitamin action, a type of experimental inquiry which involved an analogous shift of emphasis – away from the purely physiological and clinical studies of earlier workers.

Biochemical aspects of Milk formation

Setting aside however the question of hormonal involve-ment in the biochemical conversions taking place in the mammary gland – since we know so little about this aspect of our subject – it will be of interest to consider just what is known about these changes from the purely chemical point of view; what is known in other words of the intermediary metabolism of the functioning mammary gland. We have already observed that the major constituents of milk are of specific occurrence in this fluid, and we must therefore regard the alveolar cell as one undertaking multiple activities, by which precursors arriving at the cell by way of the blood stream are transformed into the characteristic milk substances. It is clear that milk is not formed by simple physical processes of diffusion, filtration through a cell wall, or the selective absorption of milk constituents already available in the body; its formation requires intense and specific chemical activity within the alveolar cell.

Various methods have been adopted for discovering what substances, taken up from the blood by the mammary gland, act as the raw materials of these transformations. The most obvious method is to analyse the blood entering the gland by way of the mammary artery and to compare the figures obtained for its various constituents with the corresponding values for the venous blood leaving the gland in the mammary vein. Quite clearly, if a substance "A" is present in arterial blood in concentration x mg. per 100 ml., and in venous blood in concentration y mg. per 100 ml., then we can conclude that $(x-y)$ mg. of "A" are taken up and utilized by the gland from every 100 ml. of blood which flows through it. The cow, because of its large milk production, is normally used for experiments of this kind, but since its mammary artery is not readily accessible without previous surgical intervention, and since blood from any other artery will have the same composition and will therefore serve as well, in practice such experiments usually involve the simultaneous sampling of blood from the mammary vein and either the internal iliac artery (by a rectal approach) or the carotid artery (in the neck). It is of course essential that the mammary vein should be used, since venous blood will vary in its composition according to the different metabolic needs of the organs through which it has passed.

In order to equate the uptake of any substance measured in this way with the amount of the secreted substance in the milk of which it might be deemed to be the precursor,

an estimate of the total volume of blood passing through
the mammary gland in a given time is also necessary. This
has been done by direct measurement with a flow meter
inserted into the circulation; and indirectly by calculating
the volume of blood from which there would be an uptake
of some substance, which is unchanged in its passage from
blood to milk, equal in amount to that in which it appears
in the milk during a given time. A suitable substance for
such experiments is calcium, and as an example of the
method we can calculate that if X mg. of calcium are
secreted in the milk in the course of a day, and by the
experimental determination of arterio-venous concentration
differences we find that Y mg. of calcium are absorbed by
the gland from every litre of blood passing through it,
then the volume of blood flowing through the gland in 24
hours is X/Y litres. This figure, in conjunction with the
appropriate arterio-venous measurements, can then be used
for estimating the amount of convertible precursors, such
as glucose, which are taken up by the gland in one day;
and allow us for example to compare the amount of glucose absorbed with the amount of lactose appearing in the
milk over the same period, and thus to test the likelihood
of glucose being an important precursor of the milk-sugar.
We might note incidentally that the figures obtained for
the blood-flow through the gland suggest that for every
volume of milk formed, about 450 volumes of blood flow
past the alveolar cells in satisfying their demand for milk-
precursors.

The measurement of arterio-venous differences although
so well suited in theory to the quantitative correlation of
precursors with milk constituents involves many difficulties
in practice. In particular any disturbance of the experimental animal will cause fluid exchanges which by altering
blood volume, and therefore blood concentrations, may
completely invalidate the significance of any figures obtained
by blood analyses.

However, the results given by blood sampling undoubtedly give very useful information both of a quantitative and of a qualitative kind, and they can be supported by evidence from other sources. For instance, Petersen and his co-workers in America have devised a technique whereby an isolated udder, taken from a cow at slaughter, can be connected with an artificial blood perfusion apparatus and maintained in a functioning state for some hours. The advantage of their method is that it allows the investigator to add to the perfusing blood any possible precursor he may wish to study, in any concentration. By taking samples of the blood at intervals he can watch its rate of disappearance, which in this isolated circuit is presumably equal to its rate of uptake by the gland. The technical difficulties must clearly be formidable, for not only has the artificial circulation to be oxygenated and an "arterial" pressure maintained by a pumping "heart" mechanism, but also great skill must be displayed in the speedy manipulation of the gland itself once it has been removed from the cow. At best the conditions, both as regards the state of the gland and the composition of the perfused blood, are highly artificial, becoming more and more so as an experiment proceeds, and it is not claimed that the method can ever be made to yield results of other than qualitative importance.

Observations of a similar type can equally well be made by incubating slices or "minces" of mammary tissue at body temperature with precursors which it is believed the gland might use. The conditions for such experiments have been well worked out and the techniques involved are in common use in all biochemical laboratories. The artificial blood circulation is dispensed with and only a few milligrams of tissue are needed, yet the end result – an observation upon the utilisation or non-utilisation of a given substance by the alveolar cells – is the same.

The results obtained from all these types of experiment allow us to draw certain conclusions about the derivation of the different milk constituents. It is well established that the greater part of the milk-sugar – lactose – is formed from blood glucose, the sugar which represents the normal carbohydrate currency of the body. Whether other substances from the blood are also utilized by the normal functioning gland in this connection it is difficult to tell, and until data are available on the proportion of disappearing glucose used by the gland for its energy metabolism, as opposed to lactose formation, the point will remain uncertain; the work done on tissue slices and the perfused udder, however, indicates that the alveolar cell can make use of other substances which might quite reasonably be expected to appear in the circulation, even though in small amounts.

Milk fat formation is accompanied by the disappearance of neutral fat from the blood, while the typical milk proteins, casein, lactalbumin and lactoglobulin, are believed to be mainly products of the serum globulin of the blood.

Again, however, in discovering the blood precursors of the milk constituents the biochemist is only touching the fringe of his work. The molecule of glucose, even though placed in the favourable environment of the alveolar cell, does not change at one bound, and as if by magic, into a molecule of lactose. The conversion, however simple it may be, must certainly involve the transient formation of some intermediary substances before the final product is reached. A similar ignorance cloaks our comprehension of the changes taking place in the formation of the milk proteins, though the detailed step-by-step formation of milk fat is possibly a little better understood.

When considering the formation of milk substances we

TABLE 1.

Species	Fat %	Sugar %	Protein %
Cow	4.0	5.0	3.5
Mare	1.2	6.0	2.0
Reindeer	17.0	2.5	10.0
Rabbit	16.5	2.0	10.5
Whale	44.0	1.0	10.0
Human	3.5	6.5	1.8

Composition of milk from various mammals. (Adapted from Davies, *The Chemistry of Milk*, Chapman and Hall, 1939).

cannot overlook the fact that these highly specialised biochemical units – the alveolar cells – show the widest differences in the balance of their activities as we pass from one species to another. Table 1 shows that the composition of milk from different animals varies greatly. It will be seen, for instance, that mare's milk has a very low percentage of both fat and protein, whereas these substances are present in high concentration in the milk of the reindeer and rabbit. Human milk on the other hand is remarkable for a low protein and high sugar content; yet we have seen that all these milks are secreted by cells developed by very similar, if not identical, hormonal stimuli, and also, so far as our limited comparative studies show, brought to secretion by other common mechanisms. It would be interesting to discover the underlying cause of this divergence in the relative importance of the various cellular activities; it would perhaps be not too fanciful to suggest that they might be found in slight differences in the balance of the endocrine mechanisms of lactogenesis and galactopoiesis in the different species; in other words, we might trace our comparative biochemical variations to hormonal origins. Support is lent to such a view by the fact that both anterior pituitary extracts and oestrogens given to cows in declining lactation have caused increases in the percentage of fat present in the milk, though whether this effect should be attributed to a specific stimulation of the fat metabolism of the cells or to an increased availability of neutral fat in the blood as a result of the injection of the hormone preparations, still remains in doubt.

It is interesting to note that there is an inverse relationship between the concentrations of those milk constituents concerned with tissue growth in the milk of the different species, and the times taken for the young of the same species to double their birth weight. (Table 2). An interesting illustration of this principle was recently given in New Biology by Ewer, in her article on whales. (*New Biology* 2, p. 53).

TABLE 2.

Species	Protein %	Calcium (mg. %)	Days required to double birth weight
Human	1.8	33	180
Mare	2.0	124	60
Cow	3.5	160	47
Goat	3.7	197	22
Sheep	4.9	245	15
Rabbit	10.5	891	6

Relationship between milk concentrations and time required for young to double birth weight. (Adapted from Hawk, Oser and Summerson, *Practical Physiological Chemistry*, Churchill, 1947).

The Ejection of Milk

Our consideration of the mechanisms of milk production would be incomplete if no mention were to be made of the way in which milk, formed and temporarily stored in the gland, is finally released.

It is a matter of common observation that the clinking of milk-pails in the cow-shed, the washing of udders, and other preliminaries of milking routine, are effective stimuli for the animal to "let-down" her milk, a process which involves the contractile forcing of milk from the smaller to the larger ducts and milk cisterns of the gland, from which, since their capillary resistance is much smaller, it can be more readily withdrawn.

Here, then, for the first time we have nervous influences playing a significant part in the physiology of milk production; it is believed however that the contractile activity is not the result of a simple nervous reflex action but is part nervous and part hormonal in origin, involving the stimulation of oxytocin secretion from the posterior lobe of the pituitary gland by the conditioned nervous impulses set up by cow-shed noises and activities. The hormone – oxytocin – released into the blood stream then causes the contraction of muscle fibres known to be present in the mammary gland, and the milk is "let-down" (Fig. 4).

It is of interest to note, as arising directly from this

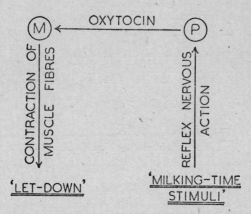

Fig. 4—Diagrammatic representation of the mechanism of 'let-down' in milk secretion. P, pituitary; M, mammary gland.

interpretation, that unusual noises in the cow-shed, rough handling of the animals themselves, or even simple alterations in the order of an accustomed milking routine, might well cause a fall in the milk obtained from an animal by interfering with its reflex nervous response and so partly inhibiting the secretion of oxytocin and complete "let-down."

Practical control of Milk Supply

From the practical point of view, one of the most important consequences of our modern knowledge of milk formation and secretion, and one depending on our realisation of the extent and nature of the hormonal processes involved, is that it is now possible for the scientist to suggest ways in which some poor lactations might be improved to the benefit both of the dairy industry and of the individual nursing mother. The hormones, as we have already seen, are ordinary chemical compounds despite their extraordinary biological activities. Not all of them are as yet available in pure form, however, and frequently they are used as extracts prepared from the glands of slaughtered animals; on the other hand some of the hormones can be synthesised by the chemist without recourse to biological material at all, and synthetic compounds have even been discovered which, while chemically distinct from the natural hormones, have all their biological activity. From this it follows that we are no longer entirely dependent upon the animal's own secretions for hormonal action, for if these should prove deficient in any individual we are sometimes in a position to supplement them by injection of hormone preparations, in the same way as the diabetic patient compensates for his lack of insulin secretion by the periodic injection of insulin prepared from the pancreatic glands of animals.

When, therefore, the lactational physiologist finds, from an inspection of the lactations of dairy animals, or indeed of the nursing mother, that yields are all too frequently poor and fall below any reasonable norm, even though the feeding and general maintenance conditions are satisfactory, he feels justified in believing that some of the lactational failures may be due to hormonal deficiencies, which could be overcome by supplementing the subject's own secretions by suitable hormone treatments; for he appreciates that optimum levels of lactation will only be reached when all the controlling mechanisms are functioning in harmony and at a maximum level of integrated efficiency. An analogy might be drawn with the diminished lactation of the undernourished animal, which can be greatly improved by additional feeding. As an illustration we may take the case of the mother who fails to provide enough milk to satisfy the needs of her new-born child. It seems very probable that since in many cases the breasts are quite normally developed, the full onset of milk-flow is being prevented by a deficiency of the lactogenic hormones of the pituitary, owing maybe to an unduly high and inhibitory level of oestrogen in the blood stream, or possibly to an increased sensitivity of the pituitary to oestrogen in the particular individual. In any case there would seem to be reason enough to hope that injections of pituitary extracts, known to contain lactogenic factors, would cause an improvement in the yield, and in fact attempts have been made to confirm this. One report claims increases in the yields – amounting to over 100 ml. daily – in a greater proportion of women receiving injections than in a second group treated by the more routine methods of massage, extra milk rations and so forth. The few well-controlled experiments done so far certainly are not enough to establish the efficacy of the pituitary injection therapy, and since moreover the pituitary hormones are not among those which can be synthesised in the laboratory, but have to be prepared from animal glands by laborious extraction procedures, it is unlikely that any great advance in this direction can be expected in the course of the next few years; but sufficient has been done at least to indicate the clinical possibilities of the method.

What is perhaps tentative and indecisive for the human, has been shown to be well-founded so far as the dairy animal is concerned. Many workers have demonstrated that increased yields can be obtained from cows in declining lactation by injecting them with pituitary preparations; the increase is maintained only so long as the treatment continues, and again any widespread application of the method is precluded by the impossibility of getting active extracts in anything like the quantities which would be required. The success of the treatment, however, points plainly to the fact that for some animals, whose lactation is of meagre duration and rapid decline, the fault lies in an insufficient secretion of lactogens by the pituitary gland. (Fig. 5).

Similar improvements in the yields of cows can be obtained by injecting the thyroid hormone – thyroxine – or by feeding the closely related substances known as iodinated proteins; but these, unlike the lactogens of the pituitary, are not specific in their action and cause a general increase

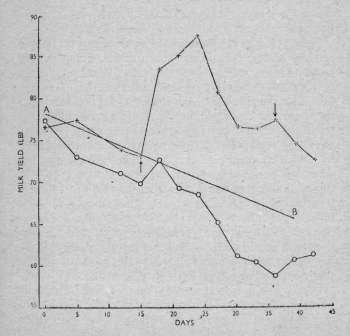

Fig. 5—The effect of anterior pituitary extract on milk production in cows.

+—+   Aggregate milk production of 4 injected cows.
o—o   Aggregate milk production of 4 untreated cows.
AB   Anticipated normal yield of injected cows.
↑   Injections begun; ↓ Injections stopped.

(*From Folley and Young, J. Endocrinol.* 2. 226. 1940, *by permission of the Authors and Cambridge University Press.*)

in the metabolism of the whole body, and not of the alveo-lar cells alone. Any improvement in yield – and increases of over 20 per cent have been recorded – may be nullified therefore by the generalised strain on the animal tending to reduce its productive life. The iodinated proteins are cheap and easily prepared, however, and provided they are used with restraint there is good reason to hope that they

will one day have a wide usefulness in improving the lactation performances of poor yielding, sluggish animals.

Perhaps the most interesting of all these practical applications, however, has been the artificial stimulation of
lactation in dry, barren cows and heifers, which on account
of their non-productivity would otherwise be of no use
except for slaughter. We have already noted that mammary
tissue can be developed in the non-pregnant animal by
treatment with the ovarian hormones; perhaps this does not
seem very remarkable so long as the statement is applied
to laboratory mammals like the rat and guinea-pig; but
when it is extended to include the cow, and the growth of
full-sized udders in one month from the start of treatment,
it certainly becomes more striking. The principles at work,
however, are exactly the same. Given suitable concentrations of oestrogen and progesterone, duct and alveolar
tissue will be laid down in the heifer just as readily as in the
rat; in fact rather more easily, for in the bovine it appears
that progesterone can be left out of account for all practical needs and a normal, or very nearly normal mammary
gland produced by oestrogen treatment alone. Fortunately,
the oestrogens happen to be hormones for which there
is a cheap and abundant synthetic substitute, and their
use as an effective agent for udder growth is not therefore
prohibited either by cost or scarcity of materials. There is
little use in even the most finely shaped udder, however, if
at the same time it is giving no milk, and it was therefore a
most welcome surprise when it was found that these artificially developed udders were also lactating without any
further treatment by specifically lactogenic hormones. In
about half the animals used in preliminary experiments of
this kind, the lactation induced was abundant, some giving
daily, and full lactation, yields equalling those of normal
parturient cows. (Fig. 6). The remainder failed to give yields
which could have justified their retention on a commercial
farm, but it is safe to prophesy a greater proportion of
successes in future work of this kind, and it is quite clear

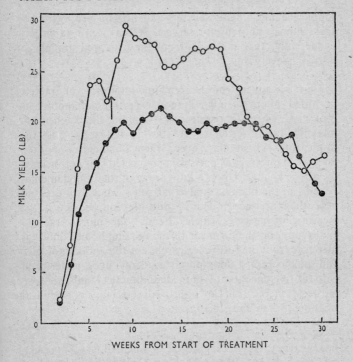

Fig. 6—Lactation curves of 2 barren cows each implanted with a tablet of oestrogen. ↑ Tablet removed. (*From Folley and Malpress, J. Endocrinol. 4. 1. 1944, by permission of the authors and Cambridge University Press.*)

that in the hands of skilled veterinary practitioners our knowledge of milk-secretory processes should, in this way, be capable of incrementing overall milk production; for the barren animal is no rarity on our farms, while frequently one encounters animals which owing to some slight anatomical abnormality are unable to breed, even though from their own pedigree they have great possibilities as first-class milk producers. Oestrogens given by injection, the implantation of hormone tablets under the skin, or by simple feeding, might well serve to bring a proportion of such animals into useful service. It has been established, incidentally, that the milk from these treated animals is normal in every way.

That so much should remain unknown, or merely hazarded, about such a common everyday commodity as milk may at first sight seem surprising, but the biochemical investigation of cellular activities is not easy, and the results of such studies, even when obtained, are often difficult to interpret as parts of a connected story of ordered metabolic change. Upon a knowledge of these fundamental systems in the mammary alveolar cell – what they do, and how they are controlled – must depend, however, the measure of success which attends our more practical endeavours on the farm, or in the nursing-home; and it is therefore from the further researches of the endocrinologist and the biochemist upon purely academic lines, undertaken without reference to any immediate practical ends, that we must expect the seeds of improved veterinary and clinical treatments eventually to appear.

FURTHER READING

Davies, W. L. (1939) *The Chemistry of Milk*. 2nd Edition. London.
Folley, S. J. (1945) *The Cantor Lectures*, '*Milk*' *No*. 2. Journal of the Royal Society of Arts, Vol. 93, p. 114.

Human Teeth and their Decay

SHIRLEY HUGHES

IN this country 95 per cent of the population suffer from some form of dental disease. This state of affairs is a big health problem by itself. It is magnified by the fact that dental disease can be responsible for many other disorders. The connection of eye infections, boils, mental disorder with diseased teeth may seem remote, but it can exist. Yet in spite of the magnitude of the problem, dental disease is very imperfectly understood. The purpose of this article is to give some background to this problem, in the form of a general account of human teeth and their ills. It will be necessary first to get an idea of the structure of teeth.

Structure

A tooth can be divided into three regions; the *crown*, the part that shows above the gum; the *root*, which is enclosed

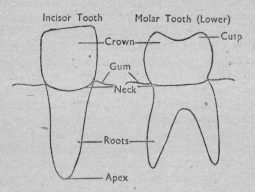

Fig. 1—Diagram of teeth showing different regions.

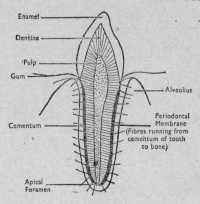

Fig. 2—Diagrammatic section of
tooth in socket, showing structure and
attachment to the alveolus.

by jaw and gum; and the *neck*, the part between crown and
root at the level of the gum margin (Fig. 1). The tooth has
a central mass of soft tissue, the *pulp* (Fig. 2), which extends
into the crown and root. The hard material of the tooth,
which forms a thick wall round the pulp, is mainly dentine
(ivory). The dentine of the crown is covered on the outside
by a layer of *enamel:* and that of the root by a thin layer of
cementum. There is a hole, the *apical foramen*, in the hard
wall of the tooth at the end of the root. Through this hole
the tissue of the pulp communicates with the tissue outside
the tooth. The tapered end of the root, which bears this hole,
is called the *apex*, though it must be admitted that most
people would naturally think of it as the base of the tooth.

   Dentine is very hard, though not so hard as enamel. It contains seventy-two per cent of inorganic salts of which the
greater part is calcium phosphate, the rest being carbonate,
fluoride and magnesium. It consists of numbers of minute
tubes of this inorganic material, called dentinal tubes, which
are set in an organic matrix of strong collagen fibres which
give toughness to the whole structure. The dentinal tubules

run from the periphery of the pulp outwards to the enamel; inside them are extremely fine dentinal fibrils which are processes of cells lying outside the dentine in the pulp (see below). There are no cells in debtine.

Enamel is the hardest substance in the body, and forms a protective mantle to the exposed part of the tooth. Ninety-six per cent of it is inorganic material, of substantially the same composition as the inorganic material of dentine, arranged in rods or prisms between which is a very sparse organic substance. This organic substance is mainly a protein with the chemical properties of keratin, the characteristic protein of nails, hair, and other epidermal structures. There are no cells in enamel.

Cementum is a modified form of bone. Like bone it contains about 65 per cent of inorganic material, and many collagen fibres. Unlike bone, most cementum contains no cells. It is the softest of the three hard substances of the tooth.

The *Pulp* is a delicate connective tissue consisting of a jelly-like ground substance in which collagen fibres, blood vessels, nerves and cells are distributed. Some cells are star shaped, some spindle shaped; and at the periphery against the inner side of the dentine is a layer of closely packed elongated cells, their long axes at right angles to the surface. These are *odontoblasts*, and they are responsible for laying down the dentine during the development of the tooth, and they also act as a defence mechanism by forming new dentine when the tooth is injured or worn. The teeth of old people, for instance, gradually wear down, but some new dentine is formed by the odontoblasts to protect the pulp. Enamel unfortunately is not regenerated in this way. The dentinal fibrils which are found in the dentine, and often penetrate a very short way into the enamel, are extensions of the odontoblasts. The function of these fibrils is not yet clear. They may be concerned with chemical processes which go on in the dentine, and they may be responsible for sensations of pain.

Attachment of Tooth. The root of a tooth is roughly two

thirds of its total length, and it is set in a socket (alveolus)
in the bone of the jaw. Between the tooth and the wall of
the alveolus is a thin soft layer of connective tissue called
the *periodontal membrane*, consisting mainly of collagen
fibres. The tooth is held in position by some of these fibres
which are anchored on one side to the cementum and on the
other side to the bone. These fibres allow the tooth minute
movement during mastication. The tooth is therefore not
fused to the jawbone, but is attached by what is strictly
speaking a joint with very limited movement.

Radio-active tracers. The hard tissue of teeth, so largely
composed of inorganic material, might be thought of as
inert, and most unlikely to undergo the continual changes
(metabolism) which occur in most parts of the body. It
has been shown, however, by means of radio-active tracers
that though the general structure of a tooth remains the
same, the individual atoms are not laid down once and for
all, but are always coming and going. Some work has been
done with radio-active phosphorus, which has been administered in different ways, by mouth, injected, or painted on
teeth. Cats and dogs have been used mainly for these
experiments, but a few have been performed on human
beings. After administration the teeth of these animals and
men were examined at intervals for the presence of radio-
phosphorus. It was detected in the cementum, dentine and
enamel, the latter containing the least amount. Even teeth
in which the pulps had been removed or destroyed were
found to have some traces of radio-phosphorus though
much less than the live tooth. These experiments on pulp-
less teeth show that the main interchange of mineral matter
takes place through the pulp while a small interchange
occurs, it has been suggested, through the cementum.

Development
The development of teeth in all vertebrates is essentially
the same, with slight modifications in the different groups.
The description given here applies to man and generally to

all mammals. The various layers of the tooth are first
formed in soft tissues before any hard material is deposited.
In the human embryo, the first signs of tooth formation appear about the forty-fifth day as a thickening
of the epithelium of the mouth. This thickening grows
down into the jaws, forming a solid band along them called
the dental lamina. At intervals, on the side nearest the cheeks
and lips, little bud-shaped thickenings appear. These will
form the temporary or milk teeth. The permanent or second
teeth are later formed on the other side of the tooth band,
that is on the tongue side. The tooth germs gradually
become bell-shaped, and at the same time the cells in the
tissue beneath begin to pack themselves closely within. The
hollow bell-shaped structure derived from the mouth
epithelium is the *enamel organ*, and the tissue inside it is

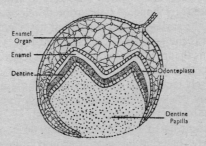

Fig. 3—Diagrammatic section of
developing tooth.

the *dentine papilla* or the future pulp (Fig. 3). The enamel
organ has two functions to perform, for it both shapes the
crown of the tooth, and invests it with enamel. The teeth of
some animals have no enamel, and in their development
the enamel organ serves only to determine the form of the
tooth. The dentine papilla by now has both blood vessels
and nerves, and at a later stage the cells on its periphery,
that is nearest the enamel organ, become columnar. They
are the odontoblasts or dentine-forming cells. Next, in the

development of a molar tooth, the internal layer of the enamel organ is thrown into folds which outline the future cusps, that is the projections of the crown of the tooth. The odontoblasts follows these folds, and so the dentine and enamel are formed by their respective layers of cells according to the pattern of the tooth set by the enamel organ. The tooth then works its way up to the surface of the mouth and as it does so the tip of the enamel organ gradually disappears. When the root is formed the rest of the enamel organ disappears and its place is taken by large cells which cover the root with cementum. The first signs of the formation of the permanent tooth are seen in a four months old embryo; they begin to calcify just before birth and erupt at about six years, but are not fully calcified before nine years.

The bones of the jaw are formed at the same time as the teeth, and by the time the latter are ready to erupt they are partly covered by bone. As the root develops the tooth approaches the surface of the jaw and at first sight it would seem that it is the growth of the root that forces the tooth to erupt. This theory is however disputed. It has been shown for instance that teeth with stunted roots can erupt and that conversely teeth with complete roots can remain in the jaw for many years and then suddenly begin to erupt. The true cause of tooth eruption is not yet known.

The question as to whether teeth can develop isolated from the jaw is one that has always aroused a great deal of interest. If tooth germs transplanted into different parts of the body, or grown completely isolated, developed normally, some of the processes concerned would be open to analysis. The interaction of the various parts could be studied, particularly by altering the position of various parts of the organ.

The grafting under experimental conditions of living tooth germs into other parts of the body has proved to be possible, and also the development of these germs when completely isolated from the body.

As early as 1874 the first known of these experiments were

performed by two Frenchmen, Legros and Magitot, who removed tooth germs from puppies 20 hours after birth, and grafted them under the skin of adult dogs. These grafts survived and formed little teeth. As these experiments were done in the days before aseptic surgery the results obtained were very remarkable. Sixty years later the next work on grafting teeth was done by Huggins, McCarroll, and Dahlberg in America. They removed unerupted canine teeth of puppies between the ages of 3 and 6 weeks and grafted them into the abdominal walls and thighs of the same animals. These workers also grafted the dentine papilla and the enamel organs separately. Grafts of the dentine papilla alone produced dentine in irregular bands. As stated before, one function of the enamel organ is to determine the form of the future tooth, and so in its absence the dentine has no regular shape. The isolated enamel organ failed to form any enamel.

Growth of teeth as tissue cultures. In 1936-9 the author showed that embryonic tooth germs would develop if isolated completely from the body, as tissue cultures. Tooth germs were taken from embryo rats and rabbits and placed in a nutrient medium of blood plasma in a small covered dish and incubated at body temperature. Plasma is blood minus the red corpuscles, and is clotted by the juice extracted from an embryo, which also supplies substances promoting growth. The tooth germs were placed in a fresh nutrient medium every 72 hours. The strictest aseptic precautions are necessary in this type of work, for none of the defences of the whole animal against infection are present in tissue cultures. It was found that cultures of very young tooth germs consisting of enamel organ and dentine papilla developed normally, except that there was little growth in size. Odontoblasts were formed and laid down a regular layer of dentine. In some cultures, a thin layer of enamel appeared. If the enamel organ was eliminated from the germ, dentine was formed in a very irregular manner, confirming the conclusion of the American workers on grafts. Molar tooth germs which had not yet formed their cusps were cultivated, and although removed from the influence of the body, they developed cusps normal in shape, number and arrangement. This shows that the factors responsible for the development of cusps are intrinsic to the tooth germ. In another experiment molar tooth germs were taken before cusps had formed and cut into two. The separate pieces were then cultured and cusps were seen to appear. If the tooth germ was isolated and halved several days before cusps were due, then each half formed a small complete tooth. If an older germ was halved, only a day before the development of cusps, then each piece formed its respective half of the tooth.

*

The fact that embryonic teeth can survive so successfully when isolated in tissue culture or when transplanted to other parts of the body, raises the question whether a lost tooth could be put back, or replaced by another.

It has recently been said that it is possible to extract a number of teeth from a mouth, clean them up, and put them back, with some prospect of them staying there. But while it is occasionally possible for a re-inserted tooth to remain in position for a few years, it usually falls out before long or has to be extracted. In a socket from which a tooth has been extracted and then replaced, new bone may form which temporarily keeps the tooth in place. But the periodontal membrane and its fibres connecting the tooth to the bone have been destroyed, and apparently cannot be replaced. The tooth has therefore no normal attachment to the jaw; it is just wedged in and sooner or later comes adrift. Another reason for the failure of retention, is that the tooth dies through interruption of its blood supply which is not replaced. Ultimately this dead mass will become infected.

Possibilities of replacing one's missing teeth by somebody else's have unfortunately no experimental backing. It must be remembered that transplantation of any kind between individuals usually meets with great difficulties. The body reacts to foreign tissue as it does to invading bacteria, by developing immunity which can ultimately destroy the transplant.

Dental Decay

Far the most important disease of teeth is *caries* or dental decay. Caries is the disintegration of the hard substances of the teeth, enamel and dentine, directly or indirectly by bacterial action. Caries starts in a very small area of the tooth, and the carious patch or cavity increases in size until it finally reaches the pulp cavity. (Fig. 4). The dentine being

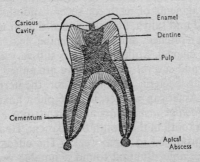

Fig. 4—Diagrammatic section of molar tooth showing caries affecting enamel, dentine, and pulp.

softer than the enamel and tubular in structure, decays faster than enamel. As the dentine softens and disappears, the enamel loses its support and breaks down. Finally the decayed area, reaching the pulp cavity, introduces bacteria into it, and causes inflammation and death of the pulp. The bacteria then pass through the apical foramen, causing disintegration of the surrounding tissues resulting in an apical or dental abscess (gum-boil).

The cause of caries is still a much disputed subject. Many of the theories of dental decay are based on slender evidence and some of the experiments on the subject have not been adequately controlled. Some theories maintain that caries is caused by food debris decaying round the tooth, others that defective nutrition makes teeth liable to attack. Still others hold that a tooth of initially sound structure is immune under any conditions and that it is defective development that provides the opportunity for bacterial invasion. These groups of theories will be considered in turn.

Decaying Food Debris. This theory originated with the chemico-parasitic theory of Miller in 1890. Miller's theory is that bacterial fermentation of food carbohydrates in the mouth produces acid which decalcifies the teeth. Miller incubated fragments of teeth for several months in a mixture of bread and saliva, and concluded that in many parts dentine was softened and the softening had sometimes included the enamel. Miller's theory is still very widely held to this day, and several workers have attempted to specify the particular bacteria responsible for the fermentation. Bunting, an American worker, in 1926 put a mixture of the bacterium *Bacillus acidophilus* and bread into a gold cup attached to a tooth in the mouth of a patient. He found that holes were produced in three weeks. The effect, however, was not invariable. Bunting found a notable exception in the case of a young woman in whose mouth two such cups were attached. Although experimental conditions were the same as those employed in other cases, her teeth seemed to be unaffected by the culture even after a period of continuous application of three months. Evidently if carbohydrate is allowed to ferment in contact with teeth, decay is not, according to this evidence, inevitable.

If decay is caused by acid produced from carbohydrates then it might be expected that differences in carbohydrate content of diets would be correlated with differences in the incidence of caries. There is some evidence that this is so. Workers in the confectionery and baking trades are very severe sufferers from dental caries. It has also been shown that in districts where flour and sugar have been recently introduced the incidence of caries has correspondingly risen. Such a district is the island of Tristan da Cunha. In 1932 the incidence of caries was found by Sampson to be 1.82 per cent of permanent teeth. Up to that date very few ships visited the island. The diet consisted mainly of vegetables, fish and eggs produced locally. With more frequent visits by ships, sugar and flour were introduced. It was found that within a period of five years the caries rate rose to 4.6 per cent of permanent teeth. This is still a low rate, but the increase is significant.

If decaying food debris is responsible for caries, teeth brushing should diminish its incidence. Clear-cut evidence about this is not available, though there are some suggestive reports. For instance, Kantorowitz, in 1936, found that Jewish children in a particular co-operative agricultural settlement in Palestine had no caries. This he considered to be due to the modern hygienic care of these children, since the Jewish children of a nearby individual settlement fed on the same diet, but not practising the niceties of modern hygiene, had a high percentage of caries. Kantorowitz maintains that oral hygiene is the most important factor in the prevention of decay. It is, however, well known that people who maintain a high standard of oral hygiene are still prone to caries while on the other hand neglected teeth are frequently healthy.

Nutrition. There has been considerable experimental work done in the field of diet. Lady Mellanby over a period of years carried out a number of experiments on dogs fed on diets deficient in Vitamin D. Her results showed that the structure of the teeth was considerably altered and that the animals were prone to caries. The addition of fat-soluble vitamins, principally D, retarded the development of carious cavities and brought about the arrest of active decay. At a meeting at Birmingham in 1937 Lady Mellanby said: 'Dental caries is not caused by eating excess of sugar, or by cleaning or not cleaning our teeth, or by eating soft food; it is not the result of omitting to eat detergent food at the end

of our meals, nor is it due to the neglect to use this, that, or
the other tooth paste ... nor shall we necessarily be free
from disease if we simply took more vitamin D in our diet
... Many factors play a part, some of which are known,
some unknown, so that it is impossible yet to guarantee
freedom from dental caries to any individual. Nevertheless,
I believe that experimental and clinical investigations suggest
very strongly that a deficiency of fat-soluble vitamins,
especially vitamin D, is the main factor which accounts for
the prevalence of dental caries in temperate zones; and I
believe it is the presence of sufficient vitamin D in relation
to other factors that is largely responsible for the comparative freedom from disease of the unspoilt natives of the
arctic and tropical climates ... ' There is sufficient evidence
to justify the stress placed on the importance of vitamin D
in the formation and maintenance of normal tooth structures. Yet other investigators have produced results con-
trary to these conclusions.

Marshall Day made a series of investigations in the
Kangra District of the Punjab. The report that was published by the Punjab Health Department on his work says
that – 'Diets are ill-balanced, consisting mainly of cereals
and containing a minimum of the protective foods, viz.
milk and milk products, green vegetables and fruit. Animal
fat is markedly inadequate in quantity, as also are vitamins
A, C and D.' The report continues 'The state of nutrition
is such as might be expected in a community in which diets
are so defective. Approximately 50 per cent of individuals
examined suffered from malnutrition in some degree.' It
was found that a very low incidence of caries was com-
patible with severe rickets, which is due to a lack of vitamin
D. The average caries incidence in children was 1.56 cavities per mouth as against 5.74 in Lahore City in India and
21.76 in Rochester, New York, U.S.A. In women suffering
from severe osteomalacia, the caries incidence was only
1.5 cavities per head. Osteomalacia is a disease due to lack
of calcium or of vitamin D associated with poor diet, fre-

quent pregnancies and long continued breast feeding. Rickety children born of these osteomalacic mothers showed a similar comparative immunity to caries.

Marshall Day concludes that a nutritionally sound diet has little bearing upon the immunity to caries, and maintains that the immunity is due to other characteristics of the diet. Meals are taken at infrequent intervals, the food possesses detergent properties and there is almost a complete absence of sugar.

Faulty Structure. Nord of Holland stresses the importance of initially sound teeth above all other factors. Nord has collected a vast amount of data on dental caries and has come to the conclusion that teeth with cracks or lamellae in the enamel inevitably will decay while those with no cracks or lamellae will not, whatever mouth conditions prevail. Lamellae are uncalcified regions of the enamel following the directions of the prisms, and usually extending to the border of the dentine. Very little is known about the cause of cracks or lamellae in the enamel and the only suggestion put forward so far is that they are due to pressure. Nord says, that bacteria are transmitted through weak places in the enamel into the dentine, attacking first the latter and later the enamel. He adds that caries can originate even in places in the mouth where the tongue has a cleansing action on the teeth. Therefore he thinks that the toothbrush also is limited in its effect.

Fish of London anticipated this view in 1931 when he wrote: 'There is a good reason to believe that caries is the result of a permeable fault in the tooth surface, occurring in conjunction with a favourable environment for the micro-organisms which initiate the caries process.'

Gottlieb, an American worker in the field, is in agreement with Nord, that caries attacks the teeth by way of the cracks and lamellae. He considers that it is possible to prevent caries by sealing the defective areas in the enamel by impregnation with silver nitrate. Unfortunately this treatment results in blackening of the tooth. There is, however, said to be a colourless preparation on the market which is also effective.

Fluorine. The fluorine content of teeth has recently been widely discussed in relation to dental decay. It has been known for many years that mottled teeth are common in certain districts, such as Maldon, in Essex, where the fluorine content of the water is high. The mottling varies from pale yellow to bright orange. These teeth have a high degree of resistance to caries which thus appears to be cor- related with the excess of fluorine in the water. It is generally believed by investigators in this field that the fluorine strengthens the tooth substance, by entering into chemical composition with the dentine and the enamel. Enamel which contains fluorine is less soluble in acid than ordinary enamel. An alternative possibility is that fluorine poisons the bacteria of the mouth since it is a potent enzyme poison. Another enzyme poison, iodoacetate, also protects against caries, and there is no evidence that this has any effect on the composition of enamel.

In certain areas of America fluorine has been added to the drinking water, and it will be of great interest to study the results of this treatment. However, fluorine is a very toxic substance and can only be used with great caution. Sodium fluoride has been tried in tooth pastes and mouth washes where it can be used in higher concentration without being toxic. It may be that by external application this substance is not long enough in contact with the teeth, and so some new method may be necessary to keep it there for longer periods. We eagerly await the results of these experiments.

*

This survey can do little more than indicate the com- plexity of the causes of caries and the incompleteness of our present knowledge. In summary, bacterial action is at the root of the trouble. Our present knowledge suggests that the activities of these bacteria are diminished or prevented by the following conditions – 'Rough' food lacking pure carbohydrates, plenty of vitamin D, fluorine in the drinking

water, careful tooth brushing, initially sound tooth structure devoid of weak places in the enamel. We do not know
how to acquire the latter, though it may be possible to seal
off weak spots. How caries will ultimately be prevented we
cannot say; but we do know that a great deal more research
will be necessary before the complicated problem is solved.

GLOSSARY

ADRENAL GLANDS: In man and other mammals, a pair of glands near the kidneys, which secrete several different hormones.

CATALYST: A substance which in minute amounts promotes chemical change without itself being used up in the reaction.

COLOSTRUM: The milk produced immediately after birth of the young. It differs in composition from the milk produced later in, *e.g.*, being especially rich in proteins.

ENZYME: A catalyst, produced by living things, of complex structure (probably always containing a protein). Every organism possesses a large number of different enzymes, each promoting only a very restricted range of chemical reactions.

HORMONE: Substance produced in minute quantity in one part of a plant or animal and transported to other parts where it exerts a profound physiological effect. In animals various hormones are produced mostly in special glands (endocrine glands) and are carried by the blood.

LACTATION: The production of milk by mammary glands.

LUMEN: Space within a tube or sac.

LYMPHATIC TISSUE: Tissue producing one of the kinds of white blood corpuscle (lymphocytes) and also acting as a filter which removes infecting organisms from the fluid (usually lymph) flowing through it.

MAMMAL: A warm-blooded vertebrate animal belonging to the group Mammalia, characterised by fur (or hair) and by the fact that its young, which develop at first within the mother, are fed after birth on milk, *e.g.* cow, dog, whale, man.

MAMMARY GLAND: Milk-producing gland of female mammals (breast, udder).

METABOLISM: The sum total of chemical processes occurring within an organism or part of an organism.

ML. Millilitre, 1/1000th of a litre, practically equal to 1 cubic centimetre.

NEUTRAL FAT: A compound of glycerol and fatty acids, *e.g.* lard.

PARTURITION: Giving birth.

PERFUSION: The artificial passage of fluid through the blood vessels of an animal or an organ. The fluid may be blood or a substitute for it.

PHOTOSYNTHESIS: The formation of organic compounds from inorganic ones by green plants, using the energy of sunlight.

PROLIFERATION: Growth by active cell-division.

RADIOACTIVE TRACER : See Tracer.

SERUM GLOBULIN : One of the kinds of protein contained in solution in the blood. Globulins are the more complex proteins, and include the antibodies.

SPECIES : Group of all animals or plants of the same kind; *e.g.* all domestic horses form one species. Similar species are grouped together into a *genus*. Similar genera are also grouped together, and so on in a hierarchy. Each species is known by a double scientific name, the first defining its genus, the second its species, *e.g. Ephestia elutella*, the cacao moth, and *Ephestia kühniella*, the mill moth, are two species of the same genus.

THYROID HORMONE : Iodine-containing hormone secreted by the thyroid gland (in the neck) which controls the rate of metabolism.

TRACER : The atoms of most chemical elements are not all alike, but are of a few different kinds called isotopes, differing in atomic weight, but not in chemical properties. Isotopes which do not occur naturally in significant amounts can be used experimentally as "tracers" : *i.e.* they can be incorporated into compounds of biological importance, administered to an organism, and their movements and changes of chemical combination determined by analysis of the organism or its products. Numerous isotopes which are radioactive can be produced artificially, especially in the atomic pile; and these make tracer work much easier, since their radioactivity makes them easily detectable.

VENTRAL : Situated at, or relatively nearer to, that side of the animal which (in the group to which the animal belongs) is normally directed downwards (in human beings, ventral side is directed forwards).

Our Contributors

Eric Ashby, Harrison Professor of Botany in the University of Manchester, is a plant physiologist. He is interested in the analysis of factors affecting growth and form in plants, and has published numerous papers on the effects of environment and heredity on plant growth. He was for 9 years Professor of Botany in the University of Sydney.

R. B. Fisher is a lecturer in biochemistry in Oxford, and an amateur of statistics. He spent much of the war as a statistician engaged in the design and analysis of bombing attacks. Despite his enthusiasm for statistics, he is not related to R. A. Fisher.

J. A. Freeman, Ph.D., is an entomologist who was working on problems of wind drift of insects before turning his attention to stored products entomology. Since 1938 he has been concerned with the development of Government research and control of stored products pests and is now Chief Entomologist in the Infestation Division of the Ministry of Agriculture and Fisheries.

E. W. J. Phillips, B.Sc., A.R.C.Sc., Ph.D., is a member of the Forest Products Research Laboratory. His researches deal with aspects of the anatomy and physiology of wood including the relationships between anatomy and the physical and mechanical properties of wood, the application of anatomy to timber identification, and the nature of the changes which take place in wood cells and their contents during the life of the tree and after its death.

G. L. Kesteven, B.Sc. (*Sydney*), worked for some time with the Fisheries Division of the Commonwealth Council for Scientific and Industrial Research in Australia. During the war he did administrative work in fisheries with various Australian government departments, and afterwards worked with UNRRA, visiting the Philippines. He has recently been appointed Regional Officer, Far East, for the Food and Agriculture Organisation.

F. H. Malpress was formerly at the National Institute for Research in Dairying, Reading, in the Department of Lactational Physiology, where he worked on problems of lactation and reproduction in the bovine. He is now Lecturer in Biochemistry at Queen's University, Belfast.

Shirley Hughes, L.D.S. R.C.S. (*Eng.*), has worked on the development of teeth. In 1939 she was awarded the Howard Mummery Memorial Prize in special recognition of her scientific work in dental histology.